# WHAT IS LIFE?
## *and Other Scientific Essays*

D0896049

# WHAT IS LIFE?

## and Other Scientific Essays

by ERWIN SCHRÖDINGER

*Doubleday Anchor Books*

DOUBLEDAY & COMPANY, INC.

GARDEN CITY, NEW YORK

Erwin Schrödinger was born and educated in Vienna. In the nineteen-twenties he achieved international status by his work on wave mechanics in the field of quantum theory. A Nobel prize winner, he is now Senior Professor at the Dublin Institute for Advanced Studies. His published works include numerous scientific papers, two books for theoretical physicists, *Statistical Thermodynamics* and *Space Time Structure,* and several books for the general reader, *What Is Life?* (1944), *Science and Humanism* (1951), and *Nature and the Greeks* (1954).

*Cover design by Miriam Woods*
*Typography by Edward Gorey*

Library of Congress Catalog Card Number: 56–9403

### *Foreword to this Collection*

In collecting essays and chapters of a less technical nature of an author whose chief occupation in life, besides the teaching of theoretical physics, was to write on extremely technical subjects, one cannot expect to attain to a well-balanced uniform whole. On the other hand, a certain amount of duplication can hardly be avoided, as may be noticed between *Nature and the Greeks* and *On the Peculiarity of the Scientific World-View*, and between *Are There Quantum Jumps?* and *Our Present Ideas about Matter*. Indeed, what provides a certain unity to the whole is that the author has in the course of the years formed a small number of definite ways of thought that are very relevant to him and to which he therefore returns again and again on various occasions.

A word should be said about the ostensible contradiction to *What Is Life?* in *Are There Quantum Jumps?* While in the former mutation (and thereby natural selection) is based on 'quantum jumps', the later essay is very critical of these discontinuous events and throws into doubt their real meaning. Well, this contradiction in words, of which I am well aware, is just one of the blank spots, mentioned in *Nature and the Greeks,* I, which the scientifically minded must prefer to leave blank rather than obliterate to future thought. From *Nature and the Greeks,* I, and still better from *Our Present Ideas About Matter,* the reader will gather how unsatisfactory and precarious our present insight into the structure of matter appears to the author.

Erwin Schrödinger

## ACKNOWLEDGMENTS

*What Is Life?:* Based on lectures delivered under the auspices of the Institute at Trinity College, Dublin, in February 1943. Published under the title *What Is Life?*, Cambridge, Cambridge University Press, 1944. The entire book is reprinted in this volume by arrangement with Cambridge University Press.

*Nature and the Greeks:* Delivered as the Shearman Lectures on May 24, 26, 28, and 31, 1948, at University College, London, and published under the title *Nature and the Greeks,* Cambridge, Cambridge University Press, 1954. Chapters 1 and 7 are reprinted in this volume by arrangement with Cambridge University Press.

*Science and Humanism:* Delivered as a series of lectures under the auspices of the Dublin Institute for Advanced Studies at University College, Dublin, in February 1950 and published under the title *Science and Humanism,* Cambridge, Cambridge University Press, 1951. Pages 1–11 are reprinted in this volume by arrangement with the Cambridge University Press.

*The Future of Understanding:* Broadcast as a series of three talks in the European Service of the B.B.C. on September 16, 23, and 30, 1950.

*Are There Quantum Jumps?:* Published in *The British Journal for the Philosophy of Science* (Volume III, Nos. 10 and 11), Edinburgh, Thomas Nelson and Sons Ltd., 1952.

*Our Present Ideas about Matter:* Published as "Unsere Vorstellung von der Materie," in *L'homme devant la science* (the proceedings of the Rencontres Internationales de Genève 1952), Neuchâtel, Editions de Bacon-nière, 1952.

*On the Peculiarity of the Scientific World-View:* Published as "Die Besonderheit des Weltbilds der Naturwissenschaft" in *Acta Physica Austriaca* (Volume 1, Section 3), Vienna, Springer-Verlag, December 13, 1947.

*The Spirit of Science:* Published as "Der Geist der Natur-wissenschaft" in *Eranos-Jahrbücher* (Volume 14, 1946), Zurich, Rhein-Verlag, 1947; published in English as "The Spirit of Science," in *Spirit and Nature, Papers from the Eranos Yearbooks* (Bollingen Series XXX. 1), New York, Pantheon Books, 1954, pp. 322–41, and reprinted in this volume by arrangement with the Bollingen Foundation, Inc., and with the Cambridge University Press.

# CONTENTS

*WHAT IS LIFE?*
*and Other Scientific Essays*

# What Is Life?

## I. THE CLASSICAL PHYSICIST'S APPROACH
## TO THE SUBJECT

Cogito ergo sum.  DESCARTES

### 1. The general character and the purpose of the investigation

This little book arose from a course of public lectures delivered by a theoretical physicist to an audience of about four hundred, which did not substantially dwindle, though warned at the outset that the subject-matter was a difficult one and that the lectures could not be termed popular, even though the physicist's most dreaded weapon, mathematical deduction, would hardly be utilized. The reason for this was not that the subject was simple enough to be explained without mathematics, but rather that it was much too involved to be fully accessible to mathematics. Another feature which at least induced a semblance of popularity was the lecturer's intention to make clear the fundamental idea, which hovers between biology and physics, to both the physicist and the biologist.

For actually, in spite of the variety of topics involved, the whole enterprise is intended to convey one idea only—one small comment on a large and important question. In order not to lose our way, it may be useful to outline the plan very briefly in advance.

The large and important and very much discussed question is:

How can the events *in space and time* which take place within the spatial boundary of a living organism be accounted for by physics and chemistry?

The preliminary answer which this little book will endeavour to expound and establish can be summarized as follows:

The obvious inability of present-day physics and chemistry to account for such events is no reason at all for doubting that they can be accounted for by those sciences.

## 2. *Statistical physics. The fundamental difference in structure*

That would be a very trivial remark if it were meant only to stimulate the hope of achieving in the future what has not been achieved in the past. But the meaning is very much more positive, viz. that the inability, up to the present moment, is amply accounted for.

To-day, thanks to the ingenious work of biologists, mainly of geneticists, during the last thirty or forty years, enough is known about the actual material structure of organisms and about their functioning to state that, and to tell precisely why, present-day physics and chemistry could not possibly account for what happens in space and time within a living organism.

The arrangements of the atoms in the most vital parts of an organism and the interplay of these arrangements differ in a fundamental way from all those arrangements of atoms which physicists and chemists have hitherto made the object of their experimental and theoretical research. Yet the difference which I have just termed fundamental is of such a kind that it might easily appear slight to anyone except a physicist who is thoroughly imbued with the knowledge that the laws of physics and chemistry are statistical throughout.[1] For it is in relation to the statistical point of view that the structure of the vital parts of

[1] This contention may appear a little too general. The discussion must be deferred to the end of *What Is Life?*, §§ 67 and 68.

living organisms differs so entirely from that of any piece of matter that we physicists and chemists have ever handled physically in our laboratories or mentally at our writing desks.[2] It is well-nigh unthinkable that the laws and regularities thus discovered should happen to apply immediately to the behaviour of systems which do not exhibit the structure on which those laws and regularities are based.

The non-physicist cannot be expected even to grasp— let alone to appreciate the relevance of—the difference in 'statistical structure' stated in terms so abstract as I have just used. To give the statement life and colour, let me anticipate what will be explained in much more detail later, namely, that the most essential part of a living cell— the chromosome fibre—may suitably be called *an aperiodic crystal*. In physics we have dealt hitherto only with *periodic crystals*. To a humble physicist's mind, these are very interesting and complicated objects; they constitute one of the most fascinating and complex material structures by which inanimate nature puzzles his wits. Yet, compared with the aperiodic crystal, they are rather plain and dull. The difference in structure is of the same kind as that between an ordinary wallpaper in which the same pattern is repeated again and again in regular periodicity and a masterpiece of embroidery, say a Raphael tapestry, which shows no dull repetition, but an elaborate, coherent, meaningful design traced by the great master.

In calling the periodic crystal one of the most complex objects of his research, I had in mind the physicist proper. Organic chemistry, indeed, in investigating more and more complicated molecules, has come very much nearer to that 'aperiodic crystal' which, in my opinion, is the material carrier of life. And therefore it is small wonder that the organic chemist has already made large and important contributions to the problem of life, whereas the physicist has made next to none.

[2] This point of view has been emphasized in two most inspiring papers by F. G. Donnan, *Scientia,* vol. 24, no. 78, p. 10, 1918 ('La science physico-chemique décrit-elle d'une façon adéquate les phénomènes biologiques?'); *Smithsonian Report for 1929,* p. 309 ('The mystery of life').

### 3. *The naïve physicist's approach to the subject*

After having thus indicated very briefly the general idea—or rather the ultimate scope—of our investigation, let me describe the line of attack.

I propose to develop first what you might call 'a naïve physicist's ideas about organisms', that is, the ideas which might arise in the mind of a physicist who, after having learnt his physics and, more especially, the statistical foundation of his science, begins to think about organisms and about the way they behave and function and who comes to ask himself conscientiously whether he, from what he has learnt, from the point of view of his comparatively simple and clear and humble science, can make any relevant contributions to the question.

It will turn out that he can. The next step must be to compare his theoretical anticipations with the biological facts. It will then turn out that—though on the whole his ideas seem quite sensible—they need to be appreciably amended. In this way we shall gradually approach the correct view—or, to put it more modestly, the one that I propose as the correct one.

Even if I should be right in this, I do not know whether my way of approach is really the best and simplest. But, in short, it was mine. The 'naïve physicist' was myself. And I could not find any better or clearer way towards the goal than my own crooked one.

### 4. *Why are the atoms so small?*

A good method of developing 'the naïve physicist's ideas' is to start from the odd, almost ludicrous, question: Why are atoms so small? To begin with, they are very small indeed. Every little piece of matter handled in everyday life contains an enormous number of them. Many examples have been devised to bring this fact home to an audience, none of them more impressive than the one used by Lord Kelvin: Suppose that you could mark the molecules in a glass of water; then pour the contents of the glass into the ocean and stir the latter thoroughly so as to distribute the marked molecules uniformly throughout the seven seas; if then you took a glass of water anywhere out of the ocean, you would find in it about a hundred of your marked molecules.[3]

The actual sizes of atoms[4] lie between about ⅕₀₀₀ and ½₀₀₀ of the wave-length of yellow light. The comparison is significant, because the wave-length roughly indicates the dimensions of the smallest grain still recognizable in the microscope. Thus it will be seen that such a grain still contains thousands of millions of atoms.

Now, why are atmos so small?

Clearly, the question is an evasion. For it is not really aimed at the size of the atoms. It is concerned with the size of organisms, more particularly with the size of our own corporeal selves. Indeed, the atom is small, when referred to our civic unit of length, say the yard or the metre. In atomic physics one is accustomed to use the so-called Ångström (abbr. A.), which is the $10^{10}$th part of a metre, or in decimal notation 0·0000000001 metre. Atomic diameters range between 1 and 2 Å. Now those civic units (in relation to which the atoms are so small) are closely related to the size of our bodies. There is a story tracing the yard back to the humour of an English king whom his councillors asked what unit to adopt—and he stretched out his arm sideways and said: 'Take the distance from the middle of my chest to my fingertips, that will do all right.' True or not, the story is significant for our purpose. The king would naturally indicate a length comparable with

[3] You would not, of course, find exactly 100 (even if that were the exact result of the computation). You might find 88 or 95 or 107 or 112, but very improbably as few as 50 or as many as 150. A 'deviation' or 'fluctuation' is to be expected of the order of the square root of 100, i.e. 10. The statistician expresses this by stating that you would find 100 ± 10. This remark can be ignored for the moment, but will be referred to later, affording an example of the statistical $\sqrt{n}$ law.

[4] According to present-day views an atom has no sharp boundary, so that 'size' of an atom is not a very well-defined conception. But we may identify it (or, if you please, replace it) by the distance between their centres in a solid or in a liquid—not, of course, in the gaseous state, where that distance is, under normal pressure and temperature, roughly ten times as great.

that of his own body, knowing that anything else would be very inconvenient. With all his predilection for the Ångström unit, the physicist prefers to be told that his new suit will require six and a half yards of tweed—rather than sixty-five thousand millions of Ångströms of tweed.

It thus being settled that our question really aims at the ratio of two lengths—that of our body and that of the atom—with an incontestable priority of independent existence on the side of the atom, the question truly reads: Why must our bodies be so large compared with the atom?

I can imagine that many a keen student of physics or chemistry may have deplored the fact that every one of our sense organs, forming a more or less substantial part of our body and hence (in view of the magnitude of the said ratio) being itself composed of innumerable atoms, is much too coarse to be affected by the impact of a single atom. We cannot see or feel or hear the single atoms. Our hypotheses with regard to them differ widely from the immediate findings of our gross sense organs and cannot be put to the test of direct inspection.

Must that be so? Is there an intrinsic reason for it? Can we trace back this state of affairs to some kind of first principle, in order to ascertain and to understand why nothing else is compatible with the very laws of Nature?

Now this, for once, is a problem which the physicist is able to clear up completely. The answer to all the queries is in the affirmative.

## 5. *The working of an organism requires exact physical laws*

If it were not so, if we were organisms so sensitive that a single atom, or even a few atoms, could make a perceptible impression on our senses—Heavens, what would life be like! To stress one point: an organism of that kind would most certainly not be capable of developing the kind of orderly thought which, after passing through a long sequence of earlier stages, ultimately results in forming, among many other ideas, the idea of an atom.

Even though we select this one point, the following considerations would essentially apply also to the functioning of organs other than the brain and the sensorial system. Nevertheless, the one and only thing of paramount interest to us in ourselves is that we feel and think and perceive. To the physiological process which is responsible for thought and sense all the others play an auxiliary part, at least from the human point of view, if not from that of purely objective biology. Moreover, it will greatly facilitate our task to choose for investigation the process which is closely accompanied by subjective events, even though we are ignorant of the true nature of this close parallelism. Indeed, in my view, it lies outside the range of natural science and very probably of human understanding altogether.

We are thus faced with the following question: Why should an organ like our brain, with the sensorial system attached to it, of necessity consist of an enormous number of atoms, in order that its physically changing state should be in close and intimate correspondence with a highly developed thought? On what grounds is the latter task of the said organ incompatible with being, as a whole or in some of its peripheral parts which interact directly with the environment, a mechanism sufficiently refined and sensitive to respond to and register the impact of a single atom from outside?

The reason for this is, that what we call thought (1) is itself an orderly thing, and (2) can only be applied to material, i.e. to perceptions or experiences, which have a certain degree of orderliness. This has two consequences. First, a physical organization, to be in close correspondence with thought (as my brain is with my thought) must be a very well-ordered organization, and that means that the events that happen within it must obey strict physical laws, at least to a very high degree of accuracy. Secondly, the physical impressions made upon that physically well-organized system by other bodies from outside obviously correspond to the perception and experience of the corresponding thought, forming its material, as I have called it. Therefore, the physical interactions between our system and others must, as a rule, themselves possess a certain degree of physical orderliness, that is to say, they too must obey strict physical laws to a certain degree of accuracy.

### 6. *Physical laws rest on atomic statistics and are therefore only approximate*

And why could all this not be fulfilled in the case of an organism composed of a moderate number of atoms only and sensitive already to the impact of one or a few atoms only?

Because we know all atoms to perform all the time a completely disorderly heat motion, which, so to speak, opposes itself to their orderly behaviour and does not allow the events that happen between a small number of atoms to enrol themselves according to any recognizable laws. Only in the co-operation of an enormously large number of atoms do statistical laws begin to operate and control the behaviour of these *assemblées* with an accuracy increasing as the number of atoms involved increases. It is in that way that the events acquire truly orderly features. All the physical and chemical laws that are known to play an important part in the life of organisms are of this statistical kind; any other kind of lawfulness and orderliness that one might think of is being perpetually disturbed and made inoperative by the unceasing heat motion of the atoms.

### 7. *Their precision is based on the large number of atoms intervening. First example (paramagnetism)*

Let me try to illustrate this by a few examples, picked somewhat at random out of thousands, and possibly not just the best ones to appeal to a reader who is learning for the first time about this condition of things—a condition which in modern physics and chemistry is as fundamental as, say, the fact that organisms are composed of cells is in biology, or as Newton's Law in astronomy, or even as the series of integers, 1, 2, 3, 4, 5, . . . in mathematics. An entire newcomer should not expect to obtain from the following few pages a full understanding and appreciation of the subject, which is associated with the illustrious names of Ludwig Boltzmann and Willard Gibbs and treated in text-books under the name of 'statistical thermodynamics'.

If you fill an oblong quartz tube with oxygen gas and put it into a magnetic field, you find that the gas is magnetized.[5] The magnetization is due to the fact that the oxygen molecules are little magnets and tend to orientate themselves parallel to the field, like a compass needle.

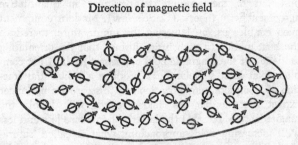

**Direction of magnetic field**

Fig. 1.   Paramagnetism.

But you must not think that they actually all turn parallel. For if you double the field, you get double the magnetization in your oxygen body, and that proportionality goes on to extremely high field strengths, the magnetization increasing at the rate of the field you apply.

This is a particularly clear example of a purely statistical law. The orientation the field tends to produce is continually counteracted by the heat motion, which works for random orientation. The effect of this striving is, actually, only a small preference for acute over obtuse angles between the dipole axes and the field. Though the single atoms change their orientation incessantly, they produce on the average (owing to their enormous number) a constant small preponderance of orientation in the

[5] A gas is chosen, because it is simpler than a solid or a liquid; the fact that the magnetization is in this case extremely weak will not impair the theoretical considerations.

direction of the field and proportional to it. This ingenious explanation is due to the French physicist P. Langevin. It can be checked in the following way. If the observed weak magnetization is really the outcome of rival tendencies, namely, the magnetic field, which aims at combining all the molecules parallel, and the heat motion, which makes for random orientation, then it ought to be possible to increase the magnetization by weakening the heat motion, that is to say, by lowering the temperature, instead of reinforcing the field. That is confirmed by experiment, which gives the magnetization inversely proportional to the absolute temperature, in quantitative agreement with theory (Curie's law). Modern equipment even enables us, by lowering the temperature, to reduce the heat motion to such insignificance that the orientating tendency of the magnetic field can assert itself, if not completely, at least sufficiently to produce a substantial fraction of 'complete magnetization'. In this case we no longer expect that double the field strength will double the magnetization, but that the latter will increase less and less with increasing field, approaching what is called 'saturation'. This expectation too is quantitatively confirmed by experiment.

Notice that this behaviour entirely depends on the large numbers of molecules which co-operate in producing the observable magnetization. Otherwise, the latter would not be constant at all, but would, by fluctuating quite irregularly from one second to the next, bear witness to the vicissitudes of the contest between heat motion and field.

## 8. *Second example* (*Brownian movement, diffusion*)

If you fill the lower part of a closed glass vessel with fog, consisting of minute droplets, you will find that the upper boundary of the fog gradually sinks, with a well-defined velocity, determined by the viscosity of the air and the size and the specific gravity of the droplets. But if you look at one of the droplets under the microscope you find that it does not permanently sink with constant velocity, but performs a very irregular movement, the so-called Brownian movement, which corresponds to a regular sinking only on the average.

Now these droplets are not atoms, but they are sufficiently small and light to be not entirely insusceptible to

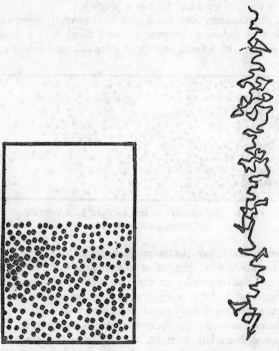

Fig. 2.  Sinking fog.          Fig. 3.  Brownian movement
                                        of a sinking droplet.

the impact of one single molecule of those which hammer their surface in perpetual impacts. They are thus knocked about and can only on the average follow the influence of gravity.

This example shows what funny and disorderly experience we should have if our senses were susceptible to the impact of a few molecules only. There are bacteria and other organisms so small that they are strongly affected by this phenomenon. Their movements are determined by the thermic whims of the surrounding medium; they have no choice. If they had some locomotion of their own they might nevertheless succeed in getting from one place to another—but with some difficulty, since the heat motion tosses them like a small boat in a rough sea.

A phenomenon very much akin to Brownian movement is that of *diffusion*. Imagine a vessel filled with a fluid, say water, with a small amount of some coloured substance

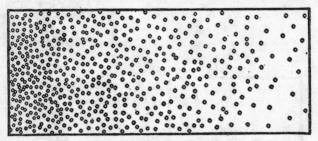

Fig. 4. Diffusion from left to right in a solution of varying concentration.

dissolved in it, say potassium permanganate, not in uniform concentration, but rather as in Fig. 4, where the dots indicate the molecules of the dissolved substance (permanganate) and the concentration diminishes from left to right. If you leave this system alone a very slow process of 'diffusion' sets in, the permanganate spreading. in the direction from left to right, that is, from the places of higher concentration towards the places of lower concentration, until it is equally distributed through the water.

The remarkable thing about this rather simple and apparently not particularly interesting process is that it is in no way due, as one might think, to any tendency or force driving the permanganate molecules away from the crowded region to the less crowded one—like the population of a country spreading to those parts where there is more elbow-room. Nothing of the sort happens with our permanganate molecules. Every one of them behaves quite independently of all the others, which it very seldom meets. Every one of them, whether in a crowded region or in an empty one, suffers the same fate of being continually knocked about by the impacts of the water molecules and thereby gradually moving on in an unpredictable direction—sometimes towards the higher, sometimes towards the lower, concentrations, sometimes obliquely. The kind of motion it performs has often been compared with that of a blindfolded person on a large surface, imbued with a certain desire of 'walking', but without any preference for any particular direction, and so changing his line continuously.

That this random walk of the permanganate molecules, the same for all of them, should yet produce a regular flow towards the smaller concentration and ultimately make for uniformity of distribution, is at first sight perplexing—but only at first sight. If you contemplate in Fig. 4 thin slices of approximately constant concentration, the permanganate molecules which in a given moment are contained in a particular slice will, by their random walk, it is true, be carried with equal probability to the right or to the left. But precisely in consequence of this, a plane separating two neighbouring slices will be crossed by more molecules coming from the left than in the opposite direction, simply because to the left there are more molecules engaged in random walk than there are to the right. And as long as that is so the balance will show up as a regular flow from left to right, until a uniform distribution is reached.

When these considerations are translated into mathematical language the exact law of diffusion is reached in the form of a partial differential equation

$$\frac{\partial \rho}{\partial t} = D \, \Delta^2 \rho,$$

which I shall not trouble the reader by explaining, though its meaning in ordinary language is again simple enough.[6]

[6] To wit: the concentration at any given point increases (or decreases) at a time rate proportional to the comparative surplus (or deficiency) of concentration in its infinitesimal environment. The law of heat conduction is, by the way, of exactly the same form, 'concentration' having to be replaced by 'temperature'.

The reason for mentioning the stern 'mathematically exact' law here is to emphasize that its physical exactitude must nevertheless be challenged in every particular application. Being based on pure chance, its validity is only approximate. If it is, as a rule, a very good approximation, that is only due to the enormous number of molecules that cooperate in the phenomenon. The smaller their number, the larger the quite haphazard deviations we must expect—and they can be observed under favourable circumstances.

## 9. *Third example* (*limits of accuracy of measuring*)

The last example we shall give is closely akin to the second one, but has a particular interest. A light body, suspended by a long thin fibre in equilibrium orientation, is often used by physicists to measure weak forces which deflect it from that position of equilibrium, electric, magnetic or gravitational forces being applied so as to twist it around the vertical axis. (The light body must, of course, be chosen appropriately for the particular purpose.) The continued effort to improve the accuracy of this very commonly used device of a 'torsional balance', has encountered a curious limit, most interesting in itself. In choosing lighter and lighter bodies and thinner and longer fibres—to make the balance susceptible to weaker and weaker forces—the limit was reached when the suspended body became noticeably susceptible to the impacts of the heat motion of the surrounding molecules and began to perform an incessant, irregular 'dance' about its equilibrium position, much like the trembling of the droplet in the second example. Though this behaviour sets no absolute limit to the accuracy of measurements obtained with the balance, it sets a practical one. The uncontrollable effect of the heat motion competes with the effect of the force to be measured and makes the single deflection observed insignificant. You have to multiply observations, in order to eliminate the effect of the Brownian movement of your instrument. This example is, I think, particularly illuminating in our present investigation. For our organs of sense, after all, are a kind of instrument. We can see how useless they would be if they became too sensitive.

## 10. *The √n rule*

So much for examples, for the present. I will merely add that there is not one law of physics or chemistry, of those that are relevant within an organism or in its interactions with its environment, that I might not choose as an example. The detailed explanation might be more complicated, but the salient point would always be the same and thus the description would become monotonous.

But I should like to add one very important quantitative statement concerning the degree of inaccuracy to be expected in any physical law, the so-called $\sqrt{n}$ law. I will first illustrate it by a simple example and then generalize it.

If I tell you that a certain gas under certain conditions of pressure and temperature has a certain density, and if I expressed this by saying that within a certain volume (of a size relevant for some experiment) there are under these conditions just $n$ molecules of the gas, then you might be sure that if you could test my statement in a particular moment of time, you would find it inaccurate, the departure being of the order of $\sqrt{n}$. Hence if the number $n = 100$, you would find a departure of about 10, thus relative error $= 10\%$. But if $n = 1$ million, you would be likely to find a departure of about 1000, thus relative error $= \frac{1}{10}\%$. Now, roughly speaking, this statistical law is quite general. The laws of physics and physical chemistry are inaccurate within a probable relative error of the order of $1/\sqrt{n}$, where $n$ is the number of molecules that co-operate to bring about that law—to produce its validity within such regions of space or time (or both) that matter, for some considerations or for some particular experiment.

You see from this again that an organism must have a comparatively gross structure in order to enjoy the benefit of fairly accurate laws, both for its internal life and for its interplay with the external world. For otherwise the number of co-operating particles would be too small, the 'law' too inaccurate. The particularly exigent demand is the square root. For though a million is a reasonably large number, an accuracy of just 1 in 1000 is not overwhelmingly good, if a thing claims the dignity of being a 'Law of Nature'.

## II. THE HEREDITARY MECHANISM

> Das Sein ist ewig; denn Gesetze
> Bewahren die lebend'gen Schätze,
> Aus welchen sich das All geschmückt.[7]
>> GOETHE

### 11. *The classical physicist's expectation, far from being trivial, is wrong*

Thus we have come to the conclusion that an organism and all the biologically relevant processes that it experiences must have an extremely 'many-atomic' structure and must be safeguarded against haphazard, 'single-atomic' events attaining too great importance. That, the 'naïve physicist' tells us, is essential, so that the organism may, so to speak, have sufficiently accurate physical laws on which to draw for setting up its marvellously regular and well-ordered working. How do these conclusions, reached, biologically speaking, *a priori* (that is, from the purely physical point of view), fit in with actual biological facts?

At first sight one is inclined to think that the conclusions are little more than trivial. A biologist of, say, thirty years ago might have said that, although it was quite suitable for a popular lecturer to emphasize the importance, in the organism as elsewhere, of statistical physics, the point was, in fact, rather a familiar truism. For, naturally, not only the body of an adult individual of any higher

[7] Being is eternal; for laws there are to conserve the treasures of life on which the Universe draws for beauty.

species, but every single cell composing it, contains a 'cosmical' number of single atoms of every kind. And every particular physiological process that we observe, either within the cell or in its interaction with the environment, appears—or appeared thirty years ago—to involve such enormous numbers of single atoms and single atomic processes that all the relevant laws of physics and phyical chemistry would be safeguarded even under the very exacting demands of statistical physics in respect of 'large numbers'; this demand I illustrated just now by the $\sqrt{n}$ rule.

To-day, we know that this opinion would have been a mistake. As we shall presently see, incredibly small groups of atoms, much too small to display exact statistical laws, do play a dominating role in the very orderly and lawful events within a living organism. They have control of the observable large-scale features which the organism acquires in the course of its development, they determine important characteristics of its functioning; and in all this very sharp and very strict biological laws are displayed.

I must begin with giving a brief summary of the situation in biology, more especially in genetics—in other words, I have to summarize the present state of knowledge in a subject of which I am not a master. This cannot be helped and I apologize, particularly to any biologist, for the dilettante character of my summary. On the other hand, I beg leave to put the prevailing ideas before you more or less dogmatically. A poor theoretical physicist could not be expected to produce anything like a competent survey of the experimental evidence, which consists of a large number of long and beautifully interwoven series of breeding experiments of truly unprecedented ingenuity, on the one hand, and of direct observations of the living cell, conducted with all the refinement of modern microscopy, on the other.

## 12. The hereditary code-script (chromosomes)

Let me use the word 'pattern' of an organism in the sense in which the biologist calls it 'the four-dimensional pattern', meaning not only the structure and functioning of that organism in the adult, or in any other particular stage, but the whole of its ontogenetic development from the fertilized egg cell to the stage of maturity, when the organism begins to reproduce itself. Now, this whole four-dimensional pattern is known to be determined by the structure of that one cell, the fertilized egg. Moreover, we know that it is essentially determined by the structure of only a small part of that cell, its nucleus. This nucleus, in the ordinary 'resting state' of the cell, usually appears as a network of chromatine,[8] distributed over the cell. But in the vitally important processes of cell division (mitosis and meiosis, see below) it is seen to consist of a set of particles, usually fibre-shaped or rod-like, called the chromosomes, which number 8 or 12 or, in man, 48. But I ought really to have written these illustrative numbers as $2 \times 4$, $2 \times 6, \ldots , 2 \times 24, \ldots$ , and I ought to have spoken of two sets, in order to use the expression in the customary meaning of the biologist. For though the single chromosomes are sometimes clearly distinguished and individualized by shape and size, the two sets are almost entirely alike. As we shall see in a moment, one set comes from the mother (egg cell), one from the father (fertilizing spermatozoon). It is these chromosomes, or probably only an axial skeleton fibre of what we actually see under the microscope as the chromosome, that contain in some kind of code-script the entire pattern of the individual's future development and of its functioning in the mature state. Every complete set of chromosomes contains the full code; so there are, as a rule, two copies of the latter in the fertilized egg cell, which forms the earliest stage of the future individual.

In calling the structure of the chromosome fibre a code-script we mean that the all-penetrating mind, once conceived by Laplace, to which every causal connection lay immediately open, could tell from their structure whether the egg would develop, under suitable condidtions, into

[8] The word means 'the substance which takes on colour', viz. in a certain dyeing process, used in microscopic technique.

a black cock or into a speckled hen, into a fly or a maize
plant, a rhododendron, a beetle, a mouse or a woman. To
which we may add that the appearances of the egg cells
are very often remarkably similar; and even when they are
not, as in the case of the comparatively gigantic eggs of
birds and reptiles, the difference is not so much in the
relevant structures as in the nutritive material which in
these cases is added for obvious reasons.

But the term code-script is, of course, too narrow.
The chromosome structures are at the same time instru-
mental in bringing about the development they fore-
shadow. They are law-code and executive power—or, to
use another simile, they are architect's plan and builder's
craft—in one.

## 13. *Growth of the body by cell division (mitosis)*

How do the chromosomes behave in ontogenesis?[9]

The growth of an organism is effected by consecutive
cell divisions. Such a cell division is called mitosis. It is in
the life of a cell, not such a very frequent event as one
might expect, considering the enormous number of cells
of which our body is composed. In the beginning the
growth is rapid. The egg divides into two 'daughter cells',
which, at the next step, will produce a generation of four,
then of 8, 16, 32, 64, . . . , etc. The frequency of division
will not remain exactly the same in all parts of the growing body, and that will break the regularity of these numbers. But from their rapid increase we infer by an easy
computation that on the average as few as 50 or 60 successive divisions suffice to produce the number of cells[10] in a
grown man—or, say, ten times the number,[10] taking into
account the exchange of cells during lifetime. Thus, a
body cell of mine is, on the average, only the 50th or 60th
'descendant' of the egg that was I.

[9] Ontogenesis is the development of the individual, during its
lifetime, as opposed to phylogenesis, the development of species
within geological periods.

[10] Very roughly a hundred or a thousand (English) billions.

## 14.　*In mitosis every chromosome is duplicated*

How do the chromosomes behave on mitosis? They duplicate—both sets, both copies of the code, duplicate. The
process has been intensively studied under the microscope and is of paramount interest, but much too involved
to describe here in detail. The salient point is that each
of the two 'daughter cells' gets a dowry of two further
complete sets of chromosomes exactly similar to those of
the parent cell. So all the body cells are exactly alike as
regards their chromosome treasure.[11]

However little we understand the device, we cannot but
think that it must be in some way very relevant to the
functioning of the organism that every single cell, even a
less important one, should be in possession of a complete
(double) copy of the code-script. Some time ago we were
told in the newspapers that in his African campaign General Montgomery made a point of having every single
soldier of his army meticulously informed of all his de-
signs. If that is true (as it conceivably might be, considering the high intelligence and reliability of his troops) it
provides an excellent analogy to our case, in which the
corresponding fact certainly is literally true. The most
surprising fact is the doubleness of the chromosome set,
maintained throughout the mitotic divisions. That it is the
outstanding feature of the genetic mechanism is most
strikingly revealed by the one and only departure from the
rule, which we have now to discuss.

## 15.　*Reductive division (meiosis) and fertilization (syn-
gamy)*

Very soon after the development of the individual has set
in, a group of cells is reserved for producing at a later
stage the so-called gametes, the sperma cells or egg cells,
as the case may be, needed for the reproduction of the
individual in maturity. 'Reserved' means that they do not
serve other purposes in the meantime and suffer many

[11] The biologist will forgive me for disregarding in this brief
summary the exceptional case of mosaics.

fewer mitotic divisions. The exceptional or reductive division (called meiosis) is the one by which eventually, on maturity, the gametes are produced from these reserved cells, as a rule only a short time before syngamy is to take place. In meiosis the double chromosome set of the parent cell simply separates into two single sets, one of which goes to each of the two daughter cells, the gametes. In other words, the mitotic doubling of the number of chromosomes does not take place in meiosis, the number remains constant and thus every gamete receives only half—that is, only one complete copy of the code, not two, e.g. in man only 24, not $2 \times 24 = 48$.

Cells with only one chromosome set are called haploid (from Greek *haplóos,* single). Thus the gametes are haploid, the ordinary body cells diploid (from Greek *diplóos,* double). Individuals with three, four, . . . or generally speaking with many chromosome sets in all their body cells occur occasionally; the latter are then called triploid, tetraploid, . . . , polyploid.

In the act of syngamy the male gamete (spermatozoon) and the female gamete (egg), both haploid cells, coalesce to form the fertilized egg cell, which is thus diploid. One of its chromosome sets comes from the mother, one from the father.

Figs. 5 and 6 are to give you some idea what chromosomes look like under the microscope. I owe the photographs from which the drawings were taken to the kindness of Imperial Chemical Industries Limited and of Dr C. D. Darlington, in whose book, *The Handling of Chromosomes* (Allen and Unwin, 1942), the interested reader will find a great many more documents of a similar kind and of unprecedented beauty. In Fig. 7 I have endeavoured to give a scematic survey of the three fundamental processes of mitosis, meiosis and syngamy (fertilization), in the case of the little fruit-fly, *Drosophila,* which plays such a prominent part in modern genetics and has the (haploid) chromosome number 4. The four different chromosomes are distinguished according to the key given in inset (*a*) in which the chromosome set of a diploid

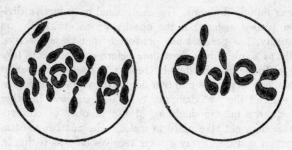

Fig. 5. Paired chromosomes in pollen mother cells of two species of *Tradescantia*. Right: Six pairs in a cell fixed and stained in acetic orcein. (After a photograph.) Left: twelve pairs in a living cell. (After a photograph taken with ultra-violet light, × 1000.)

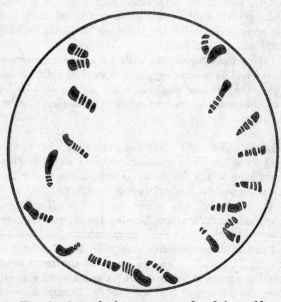

Fig. 6. Starved chromosomes reduced by cold treatment in the pollen grains of *Fritillaria pudica*. The pale bands are inert segments. (After a photograph, × 1800.)

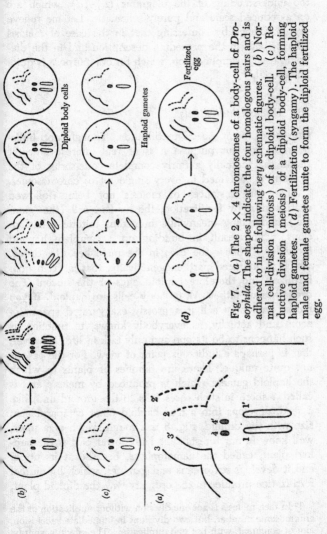

Fig. 7. (a) The 2 × 4 chromosomes of a body-cell of *Drosophila*. The shapes indicate the four homologous pairs and is adhered to in the following very schematic figures. (b) Normal cell-division (mitosis) of a diploid body-cell. (c) Reductive division (meiosis) of a diploid body-cell, forming haploid gametes. (d) Fertilization (syngamy). The haploid male and female gametes unite to form the diploid fertilized egg.

Diploid body cells

Haploid gametes

Fertilized egg

body cell is shown on a large scale. This only serves for the understanding of the diagrams $(b)$–$(d)$, which are on a reduced scale and purely schematic. Let me relieve my conscience by confessing that in the case of meiosis I have, both in the preceding description and in the diagram, used a simplification, which for our purpose is quite immaterial.[12]

## 16. Haploid individuals

One other point needs rectification. Though not indispensable for our purpose it is of real interest, since it shows that actually a fairly complete code-script of the 'pattern' is contained in every single set of chromosomes.

There are instances of meiosis not being followed shortly after by fertilization, the haploid cell (the 'gamete') undergoing meanwhile numerous mitotic cell divisions, which result in building up a complete haploid individual. This is the case in the male bee, the drone, which is produced parthenogenetically, that is, from nonfertilized and therefore haploid eggs of the queen. The drone has no father! All its body cells are haploid. If you please, you may call it a grossly exaggerated spermatozoon; and actually, as everybody knows, to function as such happens to be its one and only task in life. However, that is perhaps a ludicrous point of view. For the case is not quite unique. There are families of plants in which the haploid gamete which is produced by meiosis and is called a spore in such cases falls to the ground and, like a seed, develops into a true haploid plant comparable in size with the diploid. Fig. 8 is a rough sketch of a moss, well know in our forests. The leafy lower part is the haploid plant, called the gametophyte, because at its upper end it develops sex organs and gametes, which by mutual fertilization produce in the ordinary way the diploid plant,

---

[12] In fact, meiosis is not one division without duplication of the chromosome number, but two divisions in immediate succession, almost confluent, with but one duplication. The effect is, simply, that four haploid gametes are formed at the same time, not two only.

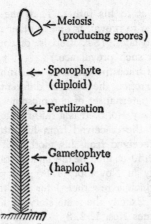

Fig. 8. Alteration of Generations.

the bare stem with the capsule at the top. This is called the sporophyte, because it produces, by meiosis, the spores in the capsule at the top. When the capsule opens, the spores fall to the ground and develop into a leafy stem, etc. The course of events is appropriately called alternation of generations. You may, if you choose, look upon the ordinary case, man and the animals, in the same way. But the 'gametophyte' is then as a rule a very short-lived, unicellular generation, spermatozoon or egg cell as the case may be. Our body corresponds to the sporophyte. Our 'spores' are the reserved cells from which, by meiosis, the unicellular generation springs.

## 17. *The outstanding relevance of the reductive division*

The important, the really fateful, event in the process of reproduction of the individual is not fertilization but meiosis. One set of chromosomes is from the father, one from the mother. Neither chance nor destiny can interfere with that. Every man[13] owes just half of his inheritance to his

[13] At any rate, every *woman*. To avoid prolixity, I have excluded from this summary the highly interesting sphere of sex determination and sex-linked properties (as, for example, so-called colour blindness).

mother, half of it to his father. That one or the other
strain seems often to prevail is due to other reasons which
we shall come to later. (Sex itself is, of course, the simplest instance of such prevalence.)

But when you trace the origin of your inheritance back
to your grandparents, the case is different. Let me fix
attention on my paternal set of chromosomes, in particular
on one of them, say No. 5. It is a faithful replica either of
the No. 5 my father received from his father or of the
No. 5 he had received from his mother. The issue was
decided by a 50:50 chance in the meiosis taking place in
my father's body in November 1886 and producing the
spermatozoon which a few days later was to be effective
in begetting me. Exactly the same story could be repeated
about chromosomes Nos. 1, 2, 3, . . . , 24 of my paternal
set, and *mutatis mutandis* about every one of my maternal
chromosomes. Moreover, all the 48 issues are entirely independent. Even if it were known that my paternal chromosome No. 5 came from my grandfather Josef Schrödinger,
the No. 7 still stands an equal chance of being either also
from him, or from his wife Marie, née Bogner.

### 18.  Crossing-over. Location of properties

But pure chance has been given even a wider range in
mixing the grandparental inheritance in the offspring than
would appear from the preceding description, in which it
has been tacitly assumed, or even explicitly stated, that a
particular chromosome as a whole was either from the
grandfather or from the grandmother; in other words that
the single chromosomes are passed on undivided. In actual
fact they are not or not always. Before being separated in
the reductive division, say the one in the father's body,
any two 'homologous' chromosomes come into close contact with each other, during which they sometimes exchange entire portions in the way illustrated in Fig. 9.
(Fig. 10 gives a drawing from microphotograph of the
event with even closer and multiple contacts.) By this
process, called 'crossing-over', two properties situated in
the respective parts of that chromosome will be separated

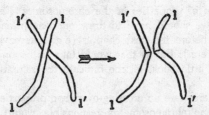

Fig. 9. *Crossing-over.* Left: the two homologous chromosomes in contact. Right: after exchange and separation.

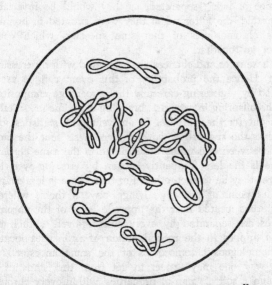

Fig. 10. Twelve paired chromosomes in a pollen mother-cell of a lily, *Fritillaria chitralensis.* The points where the loops meet mark the positions of crossing-over between the partners. (After a photograph, × 1600.)

in the grandchild, who will follow the grandfather in one of them, the grandmother in the other one. The act of crossing-over, being neither very rare nor very frequent, has provided us with invaluable information regarding the location of properties in the chromosomes. For a full account we should have to draw on conceptions not introduced before the next chapter (e.g. heterozygosy, dominance, etc.); but as that would take us beyond the range of this little book, let me indicate the salient point right away.

If there were no crossing-over, two properties for which the same chromosome is responsible would always be passed on together, no descendant receiving one of them without receiving the other as well; but two properties due to different chromosomes would either stand a 50:50 chance of being separated, or they would be invariably separated—the latter when they were situated in homologous chromosomes of the same ancestor, which could never go together.

These rules and chances are interfered with by crossing-over. Hence the probability of this event can be ascertained by registering carefully the percentage composition of the offspring in extended breeding experiments, suitably laid out for the purpose. In analysing the statistics, one accepts the suggestive working hypothesis that the 'linkage' between two properties situated in the same chromosome is the less frequently broken by crossing-over, the nearer they lie to each other. For then there is less chance of the point of exchange lying between them, whereas properties located near the opposite ends of the chromosomes are separated by every crossing-over. (Much the same applies to the recombination of properties located in homologous chromosomes of the same ancestor.) In this way one may expect to get from the 'statistics of linkage' a sort of 'map of properties' within every chromosome.

These anticipations have been fully confirmed. In the cases to which tests have been thoroughly applied (mainly, but not only, *Drosophila*) the tested properties actually divide into as many separate groups, with no linkage from group to group, as there are different chromosomes (four in *Drosophila*). Within every group a linear map of properties can be drawn up which accounts quantitatively for the degree of linkage between any two out of that group, so that there is little doubt that they actually are located and located along a line, as the rod-like shape of the chromosome suggests.

Of course, the scheme of the hereditary mechanism, as drawn up here, is still rather empty and colourless, even slightly naïve. For we have not said what exactly we understand by a property. It seems neither adequate nor possible to dissect into discrete 'properties' the pattern of an organism which is essentially a unity, a 'whole'. Now, what we actually state in any particular case is that a pair of ancestors were different in a certain well-defined respect (say, one had blue eyes, the other brown), and that the offspring follows in this respect either one or the other. What we locate in the chromosome is the seat of this difference. (We call it, in technical language, a 'locus', or, if we think of the hypothetical material structure underlying it, a 'gene'.) Difference of property, to my view, is really the fundamental concept rather than property itself, notwithstanding the apparent linguistic and logical contradiction of this statement. The differences of properties actually are discrete, as will emerge in the next chapter when we have to speak of mutations and the dry scheme hitherto presented will, as I hope, acquire more life and colour.

### 19. *Maximum size of a gene*

We have just introduced the term gene for the hypothetical material carrier of a definite hereditary feature. We must now stress two points which will be highly relevant to our investigation. The first is the size—or, better, the maximum size—of such a carrier; in other words, to how small a volume can we trace the location? The second point will be the permanence of a gene, to be inferred from the durability of the hereditary pattern.

As regards the size, there are two entirely independent estimates, one resting on genetic evidence (breeding experiments), the other on cytological evidence (direct microscopic inspection). The first is, in principle, simple enough. After having, in the way described above, located in the chromosome a considerable number of different (large-scale) features (say of the *Drosophila* fly) within a particular one of its chromosomes, to get the required estimate we need only divide the measured length of that

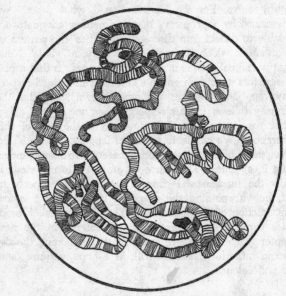

Fig. 11. Resting nucleus of a salivary gland cell in the fly *Drosophila melanogaster*. The genes have undergone eight cycles of reproduction and so occur as series of flat plates each with 256 genes. The larger genes make deeper staining bands. (After a photograph, × 1500.)

chromosome by the number of features and multiply by the cross-section. For, of course, we count as different only such features as are occasionally separated by crossing-over, so that they cannot be due to the same (microscopic or molecular) structure. On the other hand, it is clear that our estimate can only give a maximum size, because the number of features isolated by genetic analysis is continually increasing as work goes on.

The other estimate, though based on microscopic inspection, is really far less direct. Certain cells of *Drosophila* (namely, those of its salivary glands) are, for some reason, enormously enlarged, and so are their chromosomes. In them you distinguish a crowded pattern of transverse dark bands across the fibre (see Fig. 11). C. D. Darlington has remarked that the number of these bands (2000 in the case he uses) is, though considerably larger, yet roughly of the same order of magnitude as the number of genes located in that chromosome by breeding experiments. He inclines to regard these bands as indicating the actual genes (or separations of genes). Dividing the length of the chromosome, measured in a normal-sized cell, by their number (2000), he finds the volume of a gene equal to a cube of edge 300 Å. Considering the roughness of the estimates, we may regard this to be also the size obtained by the first method.

## 20. *Small numbers*

A full discussion of the bearing of statistical physics on all the facts I am recalling—or perhaps, I ought to say, of the bearing of these facts on the use of statistical physics in the living cell—will follow later. But let me draw attention at this point to the fact that 300 Å. is only about 100 or 150 atomic distances in a liquid or in a solid, so that a gene contains certainly not more than about a million or a few million atoms. That number is much too small (from the $\sqrt{n}$ point of view) to entail an orderly and lawful behaviour according to statistical physics—and that means according to physics. It is too small, even if all these atoms played the same role, as they do in a gas or in a drop of liquid. And the gene is most certainly not just a homogeneous drop of liquid. It is probably a large protein molecule, in which every atom, every radical, every heterocyclic ring, plays an individual role, more or less different from that played by any of the other similar atoms, radicals, or rings. This, at any rate, is the opinion of leading geneticists such as Haldane and Darlington, and we shall soon have to refer to genetic experiments which come very near to proving it.

## 21. *Permanence*

Let us now turn to the second highly relevant question: What degree of permanence do we encounter in hereditary properties and what must we therefore attribute to the material structures which carry them?

The answer to this can really be given without any special investigation. The mere fact that we speak of hereditary properties indicates that we recognize the permanence to be almost absolute. For we must not forget that what is passed on by the parent to the child is not just this or that peculiarity, a hooked nose, short fingers, a tendency to rheumatism, haemophilia, dichromasy, etc. Such features we may conveniently select for studying the laws of heredity. But actually it is the whole (four-dimensional) pattern of the 'phenotype', the visible and manifest nature of the individual, which is reproduced without appreciable change for generations, permanent within centuries—though not within tens of thousands of years— and borne at each transmission by the material structure of the nuclei of the two cells which unite to form the fertilized egg cell. That is a marvel—than which only one is greater; one that, if intimately connected with it, yet lies on a different plane. I mean the fact that we, whose total being is entirely based on a marvellous interplay of this very kind, yet possess the power of acquiring considerable knowledge about it. I think it possible that this knowledge may advance to little short of a complete understanding— of the first marvel. The second may well be beyond human understanding.

## III. MUTATIONS

Und was in schwankender Erscheinung schwebt,
Befestiget mit dauernden Gedanken.[14]
GOETHE

### 22. 'Jump-like' mutations—the working-ground of natural selection

The general facts which we have just put forward in evidence of the durability claimed for the gene structure, are perhaps too familiar to us to be striking or to be regarded as convincing. Here, for once, the common saying that exceptions prove the rule is actually true. If there were no exceptions to the likeness between children and parents, we should have been deprived not only of all those beautiful experiments which have revealed to us the detailed mechanism of heredity, but also of that grand, million-fold experiment of Nature, which forges the species by natural selection and survival of the fittest.

Let me take this last important subject as the starting-point for presenting the relevant facts—again with an apology and a reminder that I am not a biologist:

We know definitely, to-day, that Darwin was mistaken in regarding the small, continuous, accidental variations, that are bound to occur even in the most homogeneous population, as the material on which natural selection works. For it has been proved that they are not inherited. The fact is important enough to be illustrated briefly. If you take a crop of pure-strain barley, and measure, ear by ear, the length of its awns and plot the result of your statistics, you will get a bell-shaped curve as shown in Fig. 12, where the number of ears with a definite length of awn is plotted against that length. In other words: a definite medium length prevails, and deviations in either

[14] And what in fluctuating appearance hovers,
Ye shall fix by lasting thoughts.

direction occur with certain frequencies. Now pick out a group of ears (as indicated by blackening) with awns noticeably beyond the average, but sufficient in number to be sown in a field by themselves and give a new crop. In making the same statistics for this, Darwin would have expected to find the corresponding curve shifted to the right. In other words, he would have expected to produce by selection an increase of the average length of the awns.

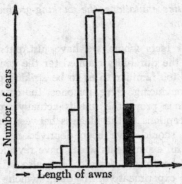

Fig. 12. Statistics of length of awns in a pure-bred crop. The black group is to be selected for sowing. (The details are not from an actual experiment, but are just set up for illustration.)

That is not the case, if a truly pure-bred strain of barley has been used. The new statistical curve, obtained from the selected crop, is identical with the first one, and the same would be the case if ears with particularly short awns had been selected for seed. Selection has no effect—because the small, continuous variations are not inherited. They are obviously not based on the structure of the hereditary substance; they are accidental. But about forty years ago the Dutchman de Vries discovered that in the offspring even of thoroughly pure-bred stocks, a very small number of individuals, say two or three in tens of thousands, turn up with small but 'jump-like' changes, the expression 'jump-like' not meaning that the change is so very considerable, but that there is a discontinuity inasmuch as there are no intermediate forms between the unchanged and the few changed. De Vries called that a mutation. The significant fact is the discontinuity. It reminds a physicist of quantum theory—no intermediate energies occurring between two neighbouring energy levels. He would be inclined to call de Vries's mutation theory, figuratively, the quantum theory of biology. We shall see later that this is much more than figurative. The mutations are actually due to quantum jumps in the gene molecule. But quantum theory was but two years old when de Vries first published his discovery, in 1902. Small wonder that it took another generation to discover the intimate connection!

### 23. *They breed true, i.e. they are perfectly inherited*

Mutations are inherited as perfectly as the original, unchanged characters were. To give an example, in the first crop of barley considered above a few ears might turn up with awns considerably outside the range of variability shown in Fig. 12, say with no awns at all. They might represent a de Vries mutation and would then breed perfectly true, that is to say, all their descendants would be equally awnless.

Hence a mutation is definitely a change in the hereditary treasure and has to be accounted for by some change in the hereditary substance. Actually most of the important breeding experiments which have revealed to us the mechanism of heredity consisted in a careful analysis of the offspring obtained by crossing, according to a preconceived plan, mutated (or, in many cases, multiply mutated) with non-mutated or with differently mutated individuals. On the other hand, by virtue of their breeding true, mutations are a suitable material on which natural selection may work and produce the species as described by Darwin, by eliminating the unfit and letting the fittest survive. In Darwin's theory, you just have to substitute 'mutations' for his 'slight accidental variations' (just as quantum theory substitutes 'quantum jump' for 'continuous transfer of energy'). In all other respects little change was necessary in Darwin's theory, that is, if I am correctly interpreting the view held by the majority of biologists.[15]

## 24.  *Localization. Recessivity and Dominance*

We must now review some other fundamental facts and notions about mutations, again in a slightly dogmatic manner, without showing directly how they spring, one by one, from experimental evidence.

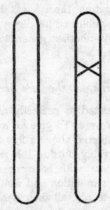

Fig. 13.  Heterozygous mutant. The cross marks the mutated gene.

We should expect a definite observed mutation to be caused by a change in a definite region in one of the chromosomes. And so it is. It is important to state that we know definitely that it is a change in one chromosome only, but not in the corresponding 'locus' of the homologous chromosome. Fig. 13 indicates this schematically, the

[15] Ample discussion has been given to the question whether natural selection be aided (if not superseded) by a marked inclination of mutations to take place in a useful or favourable direction. My personal view about this is of no moment; but it is necessary to state that the eventuality of 'directed mutations' has been disregarded in all the following. Moreover, I cannot enter here on the interplay of 'switch' genes and 'polygenes', however important it be for the actual mechanism of selection and evolution.

cross denoting the mutated locus. The fact that only one chromosome is affected is revealed when the mutated individual (often called 'mutant') is crossed with a non-mutated one. For exactly half of the offspring exhibit the mutant character and half the normal one. That is what is to be expected as a consequence of the separation of the two chromosomes on meiosis in the mutant—as

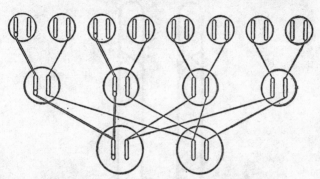

Fig. 14. Inheritance of a mutation. The straight lines across indicate the transfer of a chromosome, the double ones that of the mutated chromosome. The unaccounted-for chromosomes of the third generation come from the *mates* of the second generation, which are not included in the diagram. They are supposed to be non-relatives, free of the mutation.

shown, very schematically, in Fig. 14. This is a 'pedigree', representing every individual (of three consecutive generations) simply by the pair of chromosomes in question. Please realize that if the mutant had both its chromosomes affected, all the children would receive the same (mixed) inheritance, different from that of either parent.

But experimenting in this domain is not as simple as would appear from what has just been said. It is complicated by the second important fact, viz. that mutations are very often latent. What does that mean?

In the mutant the two 'copies of the code-script' are no longer identical; they present two different 'readings' or 'versions', at any rate in that one place. Perhaps it is well to point out at once that, while it might be tempting, it would nevertheless be entirely wrong to regard the original version as 'orthodox', and the mutant version as 'heretic'. We have to regard them, in principle, as being of equal right—for the normal characters have also arisen from mutations.

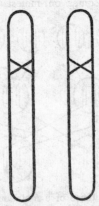

Fig. 15. Homozygous mutant, obtained in one-quarter of the descendants either from self-fertilization of a heterozygous mutant (see Fig. 13) or from crossing two of them.

What actually happens is that the 'pattern' of the individual, as a general rule, follows either the one or the other version, which may be the normal or the mutant one. The version which is followed is called dominant, the other recessive; in other words, the mutation is called dominant or recessive, according to whether it is immediately effective in changing the pattern or not.

Recessive mutations are even more frequent than dominant ones and are very important, though at first they do not show up at all. To affect the pattern, they have to be present in both chromosomes (see Fig. 15). Such individuals can be produced when two equal recessive mutants happen to be crossed with each other or when a mutant is crossed with itself; this is possible in hermaphroditic plants and even happens spontaneously. An easy reflection shows that in these cases about one-quarter of the offspring will be of this type and thus visibly exhibit the mutated pattern.

## 25. Introducing some technical language

I think it will make for clarity to explain here a few technical terms. For what I called 'version of the code-script'—be it the original one or a mutant one—the term 'allele' has been adopted. When the versions are different, as indicated in Fig. 13, the individual is called heterozygous, with respect to that locus. When they are equal, as in the non-mutated individual or in the case of Fig. 15, they are called homozygous. Thus a recessive allele influences the pattern only when homozygous, whereas a dominant allele produces the same pattern whether homozygous or only heterozygous.

Colour is very often dominant over lack of colour (or white). Thus, for example, a pea will flower white only when it has the 'recessive allele responsible for white' in both chromosomes in question, when it is 'homozygous for white'; it will then breed true, and all its descendants will be white. But one 'red allele' (the other being white; 'heterozygous') will make it flower red, and so will two red alleles ('homozygous'). The difference of the latter two cases will only show up in the offspring, when the heterozygous red will produce some white descendants, and the homozygous red will breed true.

The fact that two individuals may be exactly alike in their outward appearance, yet differ in their inheritance, is so important that an exact differentiation is desirable. The geneticist says they have the same phenotype, but different genotype. The contents of the preceding paragraphs could thus be summarized in the brief, but highly technical, statement:

A recessive allele influences the phenotype only when the genotype is homozygous.

We shall use these technical expressions occasionally, but shall recall their meaning to the reader where necessary.

### 26. The harmful effect of close-breeding

Recessive mutations, as long as they are only heterozygous, are of course no working-ground for natural selection. If they are detrimental, as mutations very often are, they will nevertheless not be eliminated, because they are latent. Hence quite a host of unfavourable mutations may accumulate and do no immediate damage. But they are, of course, transmitted to half of the offspring, and that has an important application to man, cattle, poultry or any other species the good physical qualities of which are of immediate concern to us. In Fig. 14 it is assumed that a male individual (say, for concreteness, myself) carries such a recessive detrimental mutation heterozygously, so that it does not show up. Assume that my wife is free of it. Then half of our children (second line) will also carry it—again heterozygously. If all of them are again mated with non-mutated partners (omitted from the diagram, to avoid confusion), a quarter of our grandchildren, on the average, will be affected in the same way.

No danger of the evil ever becoming manifest arises unless equally affected individuals are crossed with each other, when, as an easy reflection shows, one-quarter of their children, being homozygous, would manifest the damage. Next to self-fertilization (only possible in hermaphroditic plants) the greatest danger would be a marriage between a son and a daughter of mine. Each of them standing an even chance of being latently affected or not, one-quarter of these incestuous unions would be dangerous inasmuch as one-quarter of its children would manifest the damage. The danger factor for an incestuously bred child is thus 1:16.

In the same way the danger factor works out to be 1:64 for the offspring of a union between two ('clean-bred') grandchildren of mine who are first cousins. These do not seem to be overwhelming odds, and actually the second case is usually tolerated. But do not forget that we have analysed the consequences of only one possible latent injury in one partner of the ancestral couple ('me and my wife'). Actually both of them are quite likely to harbour more than one latent deficiency of this kind. If you know that you yourself harbour a definite one, you have to reckon with 1 out of 8 of your first cousins sharing it! Experiments with plants and animals seem to indicate that in addition to comparatively rare deficiencies of a serious kind, there seem to be a host of minor ones whose chances combine to deteriorate the offspring of close-breeding as a whole. Since we are no longer inclined to eliminate failures in the harsh way the Lacedemonians used to adopt in the Taygetos mountains, we have to take a particularly serious view about these things in the case of man, where natural selection of the fittest is largely retrenched, nay, turned to the contrary. The anti-selective effect of the modern mass slaughter of the healthy youth of all nations is hardly outweighed by the consideration that in more primitive conditions war may have had a positive selective value in letting the fittest tribe survive.

## 27.  *General and historical remarks*

The fact that the recessive allele, when heterozygous, is completely overpowered by the dominant and produces no visible effect at all, is amazing. It ought at least to be mentioned that there are exceptions to this behaviour. When homozygous white snapdragon is crossed with, equally homozygous, crimson snapdragon, all the immediate descendants are intermediate in colour, i.e. they are pink (not crimson, as might be expected). A much more important case of two alleles exhibiting their influence simultaneously occurs in blood-groups—but we cannot enter into that here. I should not be astonished if at long last recessivity should turn out to be capable of degrees and to depend on the sensitivity of the tests we apply to examine the 'phenotype'.

This is perhaps the place for a word on the early history of genetics. The backbone of the theory, the law of inheritance, to successive generations, of properties in which the parents differ, and more especially the important distinction recessive-dominant, are due to the now world-famous Augustinian Abbot Gregor Mendel (1822–84).

Mendel knew nothing about mutations and chromosomes. In his cloister gardens in Brünn (Brno) he made experiments on the garden pea, of which he reared different varieties, crossing them and watching their offspring in the 1st, 2nd, 3rd, . . . , generation. You might say, he experimented with mutants which he found ready-made in nature. The results he published as early as 1866 in the Proceedings of the *Naturforschender Verein in Brünn.* Nobody seems to have been particularly interested in the abbot's hobby, and nobody, certainly, had the faintest idea that his discovery would in the twentieth century become the lodestar of an entirely new branch of science, easily the most interesting of our days. His paper was forgotten and was only rediscovered in 1900, simultaneously and independently, by Correns (Berlin), de Vries (Amsterdam) and Tschermak (Vienna).

## 28. *The necessity of mutation being a rare event*

So far we have tended to fix our attention on harmful mutations, which may be the more numerous; but it must be definitely stated that we do encounter advantageous mutations as well. If a spontaneous mutation is a small step in the development of the species, we get the impression that some change is 'tried out' in rather a haphazard fashion at the risk of its being injurious, in which case it is automatically eliminated. This brings out one very important point. In order to be suitable material for the work of natural selection, mutations must be rare events, as they actually are. If they were so frequent that there was a considerable chance of, say, a dozen of different mutations occurring in the same individual, the injurious ones would, as a rule, predominate over the advantageous ones and the species, instead of being improved by selection, would remain unimproved, or would perish. The comparative conservatism which results from the high degree of permanence of the genes is essential. An analogy might be sought in the working of a large manufacturing plant in a factory. For developing better methods, innovations, even if as yet unproved, must be tried out. But in order to ascertain whether the innovations improve or decrease the output, it is essential that they should be introduced one at a time, while all the other parts of the mechanism are kept constant.

## 29. *Mutations induced by X-rays*

We now have to review a most ingenious series of genetical research work, which will prove to be the most relevant feature of our analysis.

The percentage of mutations in the offspring, the so-called mutation rate, can be increased to a high multiple of the small natural mutation rate by irradiating the parents with X-rays or gamma-rays. The mutations produced in this way differ in no way (except by being more numerous) from those occurring spontaneously, and one has the impression that every 'natural' mutation can also be induced by X-rays. In *Drosophila* many special mutations recur spontaneously again and again in the vast cultures; they have been located in the chromosome, as described in § 18, and have been given special names. There have been found even what are called 'multiple alleles', that is to say, two or more different 'versions' or 'readings'— in addition to the normal, non-mutated one—of the same place in the chromosome code; that means not only two, but three or more alternatives in that particular 'locus', any two of which are to each other in the relation 'dominant-recessive' when they occur simultaneously in their corresponding loci of the two homologous chromosomes.

The experiments on X-ray-produced mutations give the impression that every particular 'transition', say from the normal individual to a particular mutant, or conversely, has its individual 'X-ray coefficient', indicating the percentage of the offspring which turns out to have mutated in that particular way, when a unit dosage of X-ray has been applied to the parents, before the offspring was engendered.

### 30. *First law. Mutation is a single event*

Furthermore, the laws governing the induced mutation rate are extremely simple and extremely illuminating. I follow here the report of N. W. Timoféëff, in *Biological Reviews*, vol. 9, 1934. To a considerable extent it refers to that author's own beautiful work. The first law is

(1) *The increase is exactly proportional to the dosage of rays, so that one can actually speak (as I did) of a coefficient of increase.*

We are so used to simple proportionality that we are liable to underrate the far-reaching consequences of this simple law. To grasp them, we may remember that the price of a commodity, for example, is not always proportional to its amount. In ordinary times a shopkeeper may be so much impressed by your having bought six oranges from him, that, on your deciding to take after all a whole dozen, he may give it to you for less than double the price of the six. In times of scarcity the opposite may happen. In the present case, we conclude that the first half-dosage of radiation, while causing, say, one out of a thousand descendants to mutate, has not influenced the rest at all, either in the way of predisposing them for, or of immunizing them against, mutation. For otherwise the second half-dosage would not cause again just one out of a thousand to mutate. Mutation is thus not an accumulated effect, brought about by consecutive small portions of radiation reinforcing each other. It must consist in some single event occurring in one chromosome during irradiation. What kind of event?

### 31. *Second law. Localizing of the event*

This is answered by the second law, viz.

(2) *If you vary the quality of the rays (wave-length) within wide limits, from soft X-rays to fairly hard gamma-rays, the coefficient remains constant, provided you give the same dosage in so-called r-units,* that is to say, provided you measure the dosage by the total amount of ions produced per unit volume in a suitably chosen standard

substance during the time and at the place where the parents are exposed to the rays.

As standard substance one chooses air not only for convenience, but also for the reason that organic tissues are composed of elements of the same average atomic weight as air. A lower limit for the amount of ionizations or allied processes[16] (excitations) in the tissue is obtained simply by multiplying the number of ionizations in air by the ratio of the densities. It is thus fairly obvious, and is confirmed by a more critical investigation, that the single event causing a mutation is just an ionization (or similar process) occurring within some 'critical' volume of the germ cell. What is the size of this critical volume? It can be estimated from the observed mutation rate by a consideration of this kind: if a dosage of 50,000 ions per c.cm. produces a chance of only 1:1000 for any particular gamete (that finds itself in the irradiated district) to mutate in that particular way, we conclude that the critical volume, the 'target' which has to be 'hit' by an ionization for that mutation to occur, is only $\frac{1}{1000}$ of $\frac{1}{50000}$ of a c.cm., that is to say, one fifty-millionth of a c.cm. The numbers are not the right ones, but are used only by way of illustration. In the actual estimate we follow M. Delbrück, in a paper by Delbrück, N. W. Timoféëff and K. G. Zimmer,[17] which will also be the principal source of the theory to be expounded in the following two chapters. He arrives there at a size of only about ten average atomic distances cubed, containing thus only about $10^3 =$ a thousand atoms. The simplest interpretation of this result is that there is a fair chance of producing that mutation when an ionization (or excitation) occurs not more than about '10 atoms away' from some particular spot in the chromosome. We shall discuss this in more detail presently.

The Timoféëff report contains a practical hint which I cannot refrain from mentioning here, though it has, of

[16] A lower limit, because these other processes escape the ionization measurement, but may be efficient in producing mutations.

[17] *Nachr. a. d. Biologie d. Ges. d. Wiss. Göttingen*, vol. 1, p. 189, 1935.

course, no bearing on our present investigation. There are plenty of occasions in modern life when a human being has to be exposed to X-rays. The direct dangers involved, as burns, X-ray cancer, sterilization, are well known, and protection by lead screens, lead-loaded aprons, etc., is provided, especially for nurses and doctors who have to handle the rays regularly. The point is, that even when these imminent dangers to the individual are successfully warded off, there appears to be the indirect danger of small detrimental mutations being produced in the germ cells—mutations of the kind envisaged when we spoke of the unfavourable results of close-breeding. To put it drastically, though perhaps a little naïvely, the injuriousness of a marriage between first cousins might very well be increased by the fact that their grandmother had served for a long period as an X-ray nurse. It is not a point that need worry any individual personally. But any possibility of gradually infecting the human race with unwanted latent mutations ought to be a matter of concern to the community.

## IV. THE QUANTUM-MECHANICAL EVIDENCE

> Und deines Geistes höchster Feuerflug
> Hat schon am Gleichnis, hat am Bild genug.[18]
> GOETHE

### 32. *Permanence unexplainable by classical physics*

Thus, aided by the marvellously subtle instrument of X-rays (which, as the physicist remembers, revealed thirty years ago the detailed atomic lattice structures of crystals),

---

[18] And thy spirit's fiery flight of imagination acquiesces in an image, in a parable.

the united efforts of biologists and physicists have of late succeeded in reducing the upper limit for the size of the microscopic structure, being responsible for a definite large-scale feature of the individual—the 'size of a gene'—and reducing it far below the estimates obtained in § 19. We are now seriously faced with the question: How can we, from the point of view of statistical physics, reconcile the facts that the gene structure seems to involve only a comparatively small number of atoms (of the order of 1000 and possibly must less), and that nevertheless it displays a most regular and lawful activity—with a durability or permanence that borders upon the miraculous.

Let me throw the truly amazing situation into relief once again. Several members of the Habsburg dynasty have a peculiar disfigurement of the lower lip ('Habsburger Lippe'). Its inheritance has been studied carefully and published, complete with historical portraits, by the Imperial Academy of Vienna, under the auspices of the family. The feature proves to be a genuinely Mendelian 'allele' to the normal form of the lip. Fixing our attention on the portraits of a member of the family in the sixteenth century and of his descendant, living in the nineteenth, we may safely assume that the material gene structure responsible for the abnormal feature has been carried on from generation to generation through the centuries, faithfully reproduced at every one of the not very numerous cell divisions that lie between. Moreover, the number of atoms involved in the responsible gene structure is likely to be of the same order of magnitude as in the cases tested by X-rays. The gene has been kept at a temperature around 98° F. during all that time. How are we to understand that it has remained unperturbed by the disordering tendency of the heat motion for centuries?

A physicist at the end of the last century would have been at a loss to answer this question, if he was prepared to draw only on those laws of Nature which he could explain and which he really understood. Perhaps, indeed, after a short reflection on the statistical situation he would have answered (correctly, as we shall see): These material structures can only be molecules. Of the existence, and sometimes very high stability, of these associations of atoms, chemistry had already acquired a widespread knowledge at the time. But the knowledge was purely empirical. The nature of a molecule was not understood—the strong mutual bond of the atoms which keeps a molecule in shape was a complete conundrum to everybody. Actually, the answer proves to be correct. But it is of limited value as long as the enigmatic biological stability is traced back only to an equally enigmatic chemical stability. The evidence that two features, similar in appearance, are based on the same principle, is always precarious as long as the principle itself is unknown.

## 33. *Explicable by quantum theory*

In this case it is supplied by quantum theory. In the light of present knowledge, the mechanism of heredity is closely related to, nay, founded on, the very basis of quantum theory. This theory was discovered by Max Planck in 1900. Modern genetics can be dated from the rediscovery of Mendel's paper by de Vries, Correns and Tschermak (1900) and from de Vries's paper on mutations (1901–3). Thus the births of the two great theories nearly coincide, and it is small wonder that both of them had to reach a certain maturity before the connection could emerge. On the side of quantum theory it took more than a quarter of a century till in 1926–7 the quantum theory of the chemical bond was outlined in its general principles by W. Heitler and F. London. The Heitler-London theory involves the most subtle and intricate conceptions of the latest development of quantum theory (called 'quantum mechanics' or 'wave mechanics'). A presentation without the use of calculus is well-nigh impossible or would at least require another little volume like this. But fortunately, now that all work has been done and has served to clarify our thinking, it seems to be possible to point out in a more direct manner the connection between 'quantum jumps' and mutations, to pick out at the moment the most conspicuous item. That is what we attempt here.

### 34. *Quantum theory—discrete states—quantum jumps*

The great revelation of quantum theory was that features of discreteness were discovered in the Book of Nature, in a context in which anything other than continuity seemed to be absurd according to the views held until then.

The first case of this kind concerned energy. A body on the large scale changes its energy continuously. A pendulum, for instance, that is set swinging is gradually slowed down by the resistance of the air. Strangely enough, it proves necessary to admit that a system of the order of the atomic scale behaves differently. On grounds upon which we cannot enter here, we have to assume that a small system can by its very nature possess only certain discrete amounts of energy, called its peculiar energy levels. The transition from one state to another is a rather mysterious event, which is usually called a 'quantum jump'.

But energy is not the only characteristic of a system. Take again our pendulum, but think of one that can perform different kinds of movement, a heavy ball suspended by a string from the ceiling. It can be made to swing in a north-south or east-west or any other direction or in a circle or in an ellipse. By gently blowing the ball with a bellows, it can be made to pass continuously from one state of motion to any other.

For small-scale systems most of these or similar characteristics—we cannot enter into details—change discontinuously. They are 'quantized', just as the energy is.

The result is that a number of atomic nuclei, including their bodyguards of electrons, when they find themselves close to each other, forming 'a system', are unable by their very nature to adopt any arbitrary configuration we might think of. Their very nature leaves them only a very numerous but discrete series of 'states' to choose from.[19] We usually call them levels or energy levels, because the

[19] I am adopting the version which is usually given in popular treatment and which suffices for our present purpose. But I have the bad conscience of one who perpetuates a convenient error. The true story is much more complicated, inasmuch as it includes the occasional indeterminateness with regard to the state the system is in.

energy is a very relevant part of the characteristic. But it must be understood that the complete description includes much more than just the energy. It is virtually correct to think of a state as meaning a definite configuration of all the corpuscles.

The transition from one of these configuration to another is a quantum jump. If the second one has the greater energy ('is a higher level'), the system must be supplied from outside with at least the difference of the two energies to make the transition possible. To a lower level it can change spontaneously, spending the surplus of energy in radiation.

### 35. *Molecules*

Among the discrete set of states of a given selection of atoms there need not necessarily but there may be a lowest level, implying a close approach of the nuclei to each other. Atoms in such a state form a molecule. The point to stress here is that the molecule will of necessity have a certain stability; the configuration cannot change unless at least the energy difference necessary to 'lift' it to the next higher level is supplied from outside. Hence this level difference, which is a well-defined quantity, determines quantitatively the degree of stability of the molecule. It will be observed how intimately this fact is linked with the very basis of quantum theory, viz. with the discreteness of the level scheme.

I must beg the reader to take it for granted that this order of ideas has been thoroughly checked by chemical facts; and that it has proved successful in explaining the basic fact of chemical valency and many details about the structure of molecules, their binding-energies, their stabilities at different temperatures, and so on. I am speaking of the Heitler-London theory, which, as I said, cannot be examined in detail here.

### 36. *Their stability dependent on temperature*

We must content ourselves with examining the point which is of paramount interest for our biological question, namely, the stability of a molecule at different temperatures. Take our system of atoms at first to be actually in its state of lowest energy. The physicist would call it a molecule at the absolute zero of temperature. To lift it to the next higher state or level a definite supply of energy is required. The simplest way of trying to supply it is to 'heat up' your molecule. You bring it into an environment of higher temperature ('heat bath'), thus allowing other systems (atoms, molecules) to impinge upon it. Considering the entire irregularity of heat motion, there is no sharp temperature limit at which the 'lift' will be brought about with certainty and immediately. Rather, at any temperature (different from absolute zero) there is a certain smaller or greater chance for the lift to occur, the chance increasing of course with the temperature of the heat bath. The best way to express this chance is to indicate the average time you will have to wait until the lift takes place, the 'time of expectation'.

From an investigation, due to M. Polanyi and E. Wigner,[20] the 'time of expectation' largely depends on the ratio of two energies, one being just the energy difference itself that is required to effect the lift (let us write $W$ for it), the other one characterizing the intensity of the heat motion at the temperature in question (let us write $T$ for the absolute temperature and $kT$ for the characteristic energy).[21] It stands to reason that the chance for effecting the lift is smaller, and hence that the time of expectation is longer, the higher the lift itself compared with the average heat energy, that is to say, the greater the ratio $W:kT$. What is amazing is how enormously the time of expectation depends on comparatively small changes of the ratio $W:kT$. To give an example (following Delbrück): for $W$ thirty times $kT$ the time of expectation might be as short as $\frac{1}{10}$ sec., but would rise to 16 months when $W$ is 50 times $kT$, and to 30,000 years when $W$ is 60 times $kT$!

[20] *Zeitschrift für Physik,* Chemie (A), Haber-Band, p. 439, 1928.

[21] $k$ is a numerically known constant, called Boltzmann's constant; $\frac{3}{2}kT$ is the average kinetic energy of a gas atom at temperature $T$.

### 37. *Mathematical interlude*

It might be as well to point out in mathematical language
—for those readers to whom it appeals—the reason for this
enormous sensitivity to changes in the level step or temperature, and to add a few physical remarks of a similar
kind. The reason is that the time of expectation, call it $t$,
depends on the ratio $W/kT$ by an exponential function,
thus

$$t = \tau e^{W/kT}.$$

$\tau$ is a certain small constant of the order of $10^{-13}$ or $10^{-14}$
sec. Now, this particular exponential function is not an
accidental feature. It recurs again and again in the statistical theory of heat, forming, as it were, its backbone. It is
a measure of the improbability of an energy amount as
large as $W$ gathering accidentally in some particular part
of the system, and it is this improbability which increases
so enormously when a considerable multiple of the 'average energy' $kT$ is required.

Actually a $W = 30kT$ (see the example quoted above)
is already extremely rare. That it does not yet lead to an
enormously long time of expectation (only ⅒ sec. in our
example) is, of course, due to the smallness of the factor $\tau$.
This factor has a physical meaning. It is of the order of the
period of the vibrations which take place in the system all
the time. You could, very broadly, describe this factor as
meaning that the chance of accumulating the required
amount $W$, though very small, recurs again and again 'at
every vibration', that is to say, about $10^{13}$ or $10^{14}$ times
during every second.

### 38. *First amendment*

In offering these considerations as a theory of the stability
of the molecule it has been tacitly assumed that the
quantum jump which we call the 'lift' leads, if not to a
complete disintegration, at least to an essentially different
configuration of the same atoms—an isomeric molecule, as
the chemist would say, that is, a molecule composed of

the same atoms in a different arrangement (in the application to biology it is going to represent a different 'allele' in the same 'locus' and the quantum jump will represent a mutation).

To allow of this interpretation two points must be amended in our story, which I purposely simplified to make it at all intelligible. From the way I told it, it might be imagined that only in its very lowest state does our group of atmos form what we call a molecule and that already the next higher state is 'something else'. That is not so. Actually the lowest level is followed by a crowded series of levels which do not involve any appreciable change in the configuration as a whole, but only correspond to those small vibrations among the atoms which we have mentioned in § 37. They, too, are 'quantized', but with comparatively small steps from one level to the next. Hence the impacts of the particles of the 'heat bath' may suffice to set them up already at fairly low temperature. If the molecule is an extended structure, you may conceive these vibrations as high-frequency sound waves, crossing the molecule without doing it any harm.

So the first amendment is not very serious: we have to disregard the 'vibrational fine-structure' of the level scheme. The term 'next higher level' has to be understood as meaning the next level that corresponds to a relevant change of configuration.

### 39. *Second amendment*

The second amendment is far more difficult to explain, because it is concerned with certain vital, but rather complicated, features of the scheme of relevantly different levels. The free passage between two of them may be obstructed, quite apart from the required energy supply; in fact, it may be obstructed even from the higher to the lower state.

Let us start from the empirical facts. It is known to the chemist that the same group of atoms can unite in more than one way to form a molecule. Such molecules are called isomeric ('consisting of the same parts'; *isos* =

same, *méros* = part). Isomerism is not an exception, it is
the rule. The larger the molecule, the more isomeric alternatives are offered. Fig. 16 shows one of the simplest
cases, the two kinds of propyl-alcohol, both consisting of
3 carbons (C), 8 hydrogens (H), 1 oxygen (O).[22] The

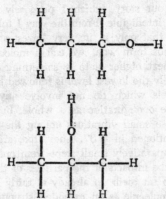

Fig. 16.   The two isomeres of propyl-alcohol.

oxygen can be interposed between any hydrogen and its
carbon, but only the two cases shown in our figure are
different substances. And they really are. All their physical
and chemical constants are distinctly different. Also their
energies are different, they represent 'different levels'.

The remarkable fact is that both molecules are perfectly
stable, both behave as though they were 'lowest states'.
There are no spontaneous transitions from either state
towards the other.

The reason is that the two configurations are not neighbouring configurations. The transition from one to the
other can only take place over intermediate configurations
which have a greater energy than either of them. To put it
crudely, the oxygen has to be extracted from one position
and has to be inserted into the other. There does not

[22] Models, in which C, H and O were represented by black,
white and red wooden balls respectively, were exhibited at the
lecture. I have not reproduced them here, because their likeness
to the actual molecules is not appreciably greater than that of
Fig. 16.

seem to be a way of doing that without passing through configurations of considerably higher energy. The state of affairs is sometimes figuratively pictured as in Fig. 17, in which 1 and 2 represent the two isomeres, 3 the 'threshold' between them, and the two arrows indicate the 'lifts',

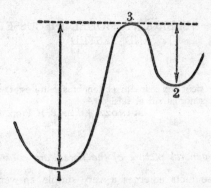

Fig. 17. Energy threshold (3) between the isomeric levels (1) and (2). The arrows indicate the minimum energies required for transition.

that is to say, the energy supplies required to produce the transition from state 1 to state 2 or from state 2 to state 1, respectively.

Now we can give our 'second amendment', which is that transitions of this 'isomeric' kind are the only ones in which we shall be interested in our biological application. It was these we had in mind when explaining 'stability' in §§ 35–37. The 'quantum jump' which we mean is the transition from one relatively stable molecular configuration to another. The energy supply required for the transition (the quantity denoted by $W$) is not the actual level difference, but the step from the initial level up to the threshold (see the arrows in Fig. 17).

Transitions with no threshold interposed between the initial and the final state are entirely uninteresting, and that not only in our biological application. They have actually nothing to contribute to the chemical stability of the molecule. Why? They have no lasting effect, they remain unnoticed. For, when they occur, they are almost immediately followed by a relapse into the initial state, since nothing prevents their return.

## V.  DELBRÜCK'S MODEL DISCUSSED AND TESTED

Sane sicut lux seipsam et tenebras manifestat, sic veritas norma sui et falsi est.[23]
SPINOZA, *Ethics*, P. II, Prop. 43.

### 40.  *The general picture of the hereditary substance*

From these facts emerges a very simple answer to our question, namely: Are these structures, composed of comparatively few atoms, capable of withstanding for long periods the disturbing influence of heat motion to which the hereditary substance is continually exposed? We shall assume the structure of a gene to be that of a huge molecule, capable only of discontinuous change, which consists in a rearrangement of the atoms and leads to an isomeric[24] molecule. The rearrangement may affect only a small region of the gene, and a vast number of different rearrangements may be possible. The energy thresholds, separating the actual configuration from any possible isomeric ones, have to be high enough (compared with the average heat energy of an atom) to make the change-over a rare event. These rare events we shall identify with spontaneous mutations.

The later parts of this chapter will be devoted to put-

[23] Truly, as light manifests itself and darkness, thus truth is the standard of itself and of error.
[24] For convenience I shall continue to call it an isomeric transition, though it would be absurd to exclude the possibility of any exchange with the environment.

ting this general picture of a gene and of mutation (due mainly to the German physicist M. Delbrück) to the test, by comparing it in detail with genetical facts. Before doing so, we may fittingly make some comment on the foundation and general nature of the theory.

## 41. *The uniqueness of the picture*

Was it absolutely essential for the biological question to dig up the deepest roots and found the picture on quantum mechanics? The conjecture that a gene is a molecule is to-day, I dare say, a commonplace. Few biologists, whether familiar with quantum theory or not, would disagree with it. In § 32 we ventured to put it into the mouth of a pre-quantum physicist, as the only reasonable explanation of the observed permanence. The subsequent considerations about isomerism, threshold energy, the paramount role of the ratio $W:kT$ in determining the probability of an isomeric transition—all that could very well be introduced on a purely empirical basis, at any rate without drawing explicitly on quantum theory. Why did I so strongly insist on the quantum-mechanical point of view, though I could not really make it clear in this little book and may well have bored many a reader?

Quantum mechanics is the first theoretical aspect which accounts from first principles for all kinds of aggregates of atoms actually encountered in Nature. The Heitler-London bondage is a unique, singular feature of the theory, not invented for the purpose of explaining the chemical bond. It comes in quite by itself, in a highly interesting and puzzling manner, being forced upon us by entirely different considerations. It proves to correspond exactly with the observed chemical facts, and, as I said, it is a unique feature, well enough understood to tell with reasonable certainty that 'such a thing could not happen again' in the further development of quantum theory.

Consequently, we may safely assert that there is no alternative to the molecular explanation of the hereditary substance. The physical aspect leaves no other possibility to account for its permanence. If the Delbrück picture should fail, we would have to give up further attempts. That is the first point I wish to make.

## 42. Some traditional misconceptions

But it may be asked: Are there really no other endurable structures composed of atoms except molecules? Does not a gold coin, for example, buried in a tomb for a couple of thousand years, preserve the traits of the portrait stamped on it? It is true that the coin consists of an enormous number of atoms, but surely we are in this case not inclined to attribute the mere preservation of shape to the statistics of large numbers. The same remark applies to a neatly developed batch of crystals we find embedded in a rock, where it must have been for geological periods without changing.

That leads us to the second point I want to elucidate. The cases of a molecule, a solid, a crystal, are not really different. In the light of present knowledge they are virtually the same. Unfortunately, school teaching keeps up certain traditional views, which have been out of date for many years and which obscure the understanding of the actual state of affairs.

Indeed, what we have learnt at school about molecules does not give the idea that they are more closely akin to the solid state than to the liquid or gaseous state. On the contrary, we have been taught to distinguish carefully between a physical change, such as melting or evaporation, in which the molecules are preserved (so that, for example, alcohol, whether solid, liquid or a gas, always consists of the same molecules, $C_2H_6O$), and a chemical change, as, for example, the burning of alcohol,

$$C_2H_6O + 3O_2 = 2CO_2 + 3H_2O,$$

where an alcohol molecule and three oxygen molecules undergo a rearrangement to form two molecules of carbon dioxide and three molecules of water.

About crystals, we have been taught that they form threefold periodic lattices, in which the structure of the single molecule is sometimes recognizable, as in the case of alcohol and most organic compounds, while in other crystals, e.g. rock-salt (NaCl), NaCl molecules cannot be unequivocally delimited, because every Na atom is symmetrically surrounded by six Cl atoms, and vice versa, so that it is largely arbitrary what pairs, if any, are regarded as molecular partners.

Finally, we have been told that a solid can be crystalline or not, and in the latter case we call it amorphous.

### 43. *Different 'states' of matter*

Now I would not go so far as to say that all these statements and distinctions are quite wrong. For practical purposes they are sometimes useful. But in the true aspect of the structure of matter the limits must be drawn in an entirely different way. The fundamental distinction is between the two lines of the following scheme of 'equations':

$$molecule = solid = crystal.$$
$$gas = liquid = amorphous.$$

We must explain these statements briefly. The so-called amorphous solids are either not really amorphous or not really solid. In 'amorphous' charcoal fibre the rudimentary structure of the graphite crystal has been disclosed by X-rays. So charcoal is a solid, but also crystalline. Where we find no crystalline structure we have to regard the thing as a liquid with very high 'viscosity' (internal friction). Such a substance discloses by the absence of a well-defined melting temperature and of a latent heat of melting that it is not a true solid. When heated it softens gradually and eventually liquefies without discontinuity. (I remember that at the end of the first Great War we were given in Vienna an asphalt-like substance as a substitute for coffee. It was so hard that one had to use a chisel or a hatchet to break the little brick into pieces, when it would show a smooth, shell-like cleavage. Yet, given time, it would behave as a liquid, closely packing the lower part of a vessel in which you were unwise enough to leave it for a couple of days.)

The continuity of the gaseous and liquid state is a well-known story. You can liquefy any gas without discontinuity by taking your way 'around' the so-called critical point. But we shall not enter on this here.

## 44.   *The distinction that really matters*

We have thus justified everything in the above scheme, except the main point, namely, that we wish a molecule to be regarded as a solid = crystal.

The reason for this is that the atoms forming a molecule, whether there be few or many of them, are united by forces of exactly the same nature as the numerous atoms which build up a true solid, a crystal. The molecule presents the same solidity of structure as a crystal. Remember that it is precisely this solidity on which we draw to account for the permanence of the gene!

The distinction that is really important in the structure of matter is whether atoms are bound together by those 'solidifying' Heitler-London forces or whether they are not. In a solid and in a molecule they all are. In a gas of single atoms (as e.g. mercury vapour) they are not. In a gas composed of molecules, only the atoms within every molecule are linked in this way.

## 45.   *The aperiodic solid*

A small molecule might be called 'the germ of a solid'. Starting from such a small solid germ, there seem to be two different ways of building up larger and larger associations. One is the comparatively dull way of repeating the same structure in three directions again and again. That is the way followed in a growing crystal. Once the periodicity is established, there is no definite limit to the size of the aggregate. The other way is that of building up a more and more extended aggregate without the dull device of repetition. That is the case of the more and more complicated organic molecule in which every atom, and every group of atoms, plays an individual role, not entirely equivalent to that of many others (as is the case in a periodic structure). We might quite properly call that an aperiodic crystal or solid and express our hypothesis by saying: We believe a gene—or perhaps the whole chromosome fibre[25]—to be an aperiodic solid.

## 46. *The variety of contents compressed in the miniature code*

It has often been asked how this tiny speck of material, the nucleus of the fertilized egg, could contain an elaborate code-script involving all the future development of the organism? A well-ordered association of atoms, endowed with sufficient resistivity to keep its order permanently, appears to be the only conceivable material structure that offers a variety of possible ('isomeric') arrangements sufficiently large to embody a complicated system of 'determinations' within a small spatial boundary. Indeed, the number of atoms in such a structure need not be very large to produce an almost unlimited number of possible arrangements. For illustration, think of the Morse code. The two different signs of dot and dash in well-ordered groups of not more than four allow of thirty different specifications. Now, if you allowed yourself the use of a third sign, in addition to dot and dash, and used groups of not more than ten, you could form 88,572 different 'letters'; with five signs and groups up to 25, the number is 372,529,029,846,191,405.

It may be objected that the simile is deficient, because our Morse signs may have different composition (e.g. $\cdot$—— and $\cdot\cdot$—) and thus they are a bad analogue for isomerism. To remedy this defect, let us pick, from the third example, only the combinations of exactly 25 symbols and only those containing exactly 5 out of each of the supposed 5 types (5 dots, 5 dashes, etc.). A rough count gives you the number of combinations as 62,330,000,000,000, where the zeros on the right stand for figures which I have not taken the trouble to compute.

Of course, in the actual case, by no means 'every' ar-

[25] That it is highly flexible is no objection; so is a thin copper wire.

rangement of the group of atoms will represent a possible
molecule; moreover, it is not a question of a code to be
adopted arbitrarily, for the code-script must itself be the
operative factor bringing about the development. But, on
the other hand, the number chosen in the example (25) is
still very small, and we have envisaged only the simple
arrangements in one line. What we wish to illustrate is
simply that with the molecular picture of the gene it is no
longer inconceivable that the miniature code should precisely correspond with a highly complicated and specified
plan of development and should somehow contain the
means to put it into operation.

### 47.   *Comparison with facts: degree of stability; discontinuity of mutations*

Now let us at last proceed to compare the theoretical picture with the biological facts. The first question obviously
is, whether it can really account for the high degree of
permanence we observe. Are threshold values of the required amount—high multiples of the average heat energy
$kT$—reasonable, are they within the range known from
ordinary chemistry? That question is trivial; it can be
answered in the affirmative without inspecting tables. The
molecules of any substance which the chemist is able to
isolate at a given temperature must at that temperature
have a lifetime of at least minutes. (That is putting it
mildly; as a rule they have much more.) Thus the threshold values the chemist encounters are of necessity precisely of the order of magnitude required to account for
practically any degree of permanence the biologist may
encounter; for we recall from § 36 that thresholds varying
within a range of about 1:2 will account for lifetimes
ranging from a fraction of a second to tens of thousands
of years.

But let me mention figures, for future reference. The
ratios $W/kT$ mentioned by way of example in § 36, viz.

$$\frac{W}{kT} = 30, 50, 60,$$

producing lifetimes of

$$\frac{1}{10} \text{ sec., 16 months, 30,000 years,}$$

respectively, correspond at room temperature with threshold values of

$$0.9, \quad 1.5, \quad 1.8 \text{ electron-volts.}$$

We must explain the unit 'electron-volt', which is rather convenient for the physicist, because it can be visualized. For example, the third number (1.8) means that an electron, accelerated by a voltage of about 2 volts, would have acquired just sufficient energy to effect the transition by impact. (For comparison, the battery of an ordinary pocket flash-light has 3 volts.)

These considerations make it conceivable that an isomeric change of configuration in some part of our molecule, produced by a chance fluctuation of the vibrational energy, can actually be a sufficiently rare event to be interpreted as a spontaneous mutation. Thus we account, by the very principles of quantum mechanics, for the most amazing fact about mutations, the fact by which they first attracted de Vries's attention, namely, that they are 'jumping' variations, no intermediate forms occurring.

## 48. *Stability of naturally selected genes*

Having discovered the increase of the natural mutation rate by any kind of ionizing rays, one might think of attributing the natural rate to the radio-activity of the soil and air and to cosmic radiation. But a quantitative comparison with the X-ray results shows that the 'natural radiation' is much too weak and could account only for a small fraction of the natural rate.

Granted that we have to account for the rare natural mutations by chance fluctuations of the heat motion, we must not be very much astonished that Nature has succeeded in making such a subtle choice of threshold values as is necessary to make mutation rare. For we have, earlier in these lectures, arrived at the conclusion that frequent mutations are detrimental to evolution. Individuals which, by mutation, acquire a gene configuration of insufficient stability, will have little chance of seeing their 'ultra-radical', rapidly mutating, descendancy survive long. The species will be freed of them and will thus collect stable genes by natural selection.

### 49. *The sometimes lower stability of mutants*

But, of course, as regards the mutants which occur in our breeding experiments and which we select, *qua* mutants, for studying their offspring, there is no reason to expect that they should all show that very high stability. For they have not yet been 'tried out'—or, if they have, they have been 'rejected' in the wild breeds—possibly for too high mutability. At any rate, we are not at all astonished to learn that actually some of these mutants do show a much higher mutability than the normal 'wild' genes.

### 50. *Temperature influences unstable genes less than stable ones*

This enables us to test our mutability formula, which was

$$t = \tau e^{W/kT}.$$

(It will be remembered that $t$ is the time of expectation for a mutation with threshold energy $W$.) We ask: How does $t$ change with the temperature? We easily find from the preceding formula in good approximation the ratio of the value of $t$ at temperature $T + 10$, to that at temperature $T$

$$\frac{t_{T+10}}{t_T} = e^{-10W/kT^2}.$$

The exponent being now negative, the ratio is, naturally, smaller than 1. The time of expectation is diminished by raising the temperature, the mutability is increased. Now that can be tested and has been tested with the fly *Drosophila* in the range of temperature which the insects will stand. The result was, at first sight, surprising. The *low* mutability of wild genes was distinctly increased, but the comparatively *high* mutability occurring with some of the already mutated genes was not, or at any rate was much less, increased. That is just what we expect on comparing our two formulae. A large value of $W/kT$, which according to the first formula is required to make $t$ large (stable gene), will, according to the second one, make for a small value of the ratio computed there, that is to say for a considerable increase of mutability with temperature. (The actual values of the ratio seem to lie between about ½ and ⅕. The reciprocal, 2·5, is what in an ordinary chemical reaction we call the van 't Hoff factor.)

## 51. *How X-rays produce mutation*

Turning now to the X-ray-induced mutation rate, we have already inferred from the breeding experiments, first (from the proportionality of mutation rate, and dosage), that some single event produces the mutation; secondly (from quantitative results and from the fact that the mutation rate is determined by the integrated ionization density and independent of the wave-length), this single event must be an ionization, or similar process, which has to take place inside a certain volume of only about 10 atomic-distances-cubed, in order to produce a specified mutation. According to our picture, the energy for overcoming the threshold must obviously be furnished by that explosion-like process, ionization or excitation. I call it explosion-like, because the energy spent in one ionization (spent, incidentally, not by the X-ray itself, but by a secondary electron it produces) is well known and has the comparatively enormous amount of 30 electron-volts. It is bound to be turned into enormously increased heat motion around the point where it is discharged and to spread from there in the form of a 'heat wave', a wave of intense oscillations of the atoms. That this heat wave should still be able to furnish the required threshold energy or 1 or 2 electron-volts at an average 'range of action' of about ten atomic distances, is not inconceivable, though it may well be that an unprejudiced physicist might have anticipated a slightly lower range of action. That in many cases the effect of the explosion will not be an orderly isomeric transition but a lesion of the chromosome, a lesion that becomes lethal when, by ingenious crossings, the uninjured partner (the corresponding chromosome of the second set) is removed and replaced by a partner whose corresponding gene is known to be itself morbid—all that is absolutely to be expected and it is exactly what is observed.

## 52. *Their efficiency does not depend on spontaneous mutability*

Quite a few other features are, if not predictable from the picture, easily understood from it. For example, an unstable mutant does not on the average show a much higher X-ray mutation rate than a stable one. Now, with an explosion furnishing an energy of 30 electron-volts you would certainly not expect that it makes a lot of difference whether the required threshold energy is a little larger or a little smaller, say 1 or 1·3 volts.

## 53. *Reversible mutations*

In some cases a transition was studied in both directions, say from a certain 'wild' gene to a specified mutant and back from that mutant to the wild gene. In such cases the natural mutation rate is sometimes nearly the same, sometimes very different. At first sight one is puzzled, because the threshold to be overcome seems to be the same in both cases. But, of course, it need not be, because it has to be measured from the energy level of the starting configuration, and that may be different for the wild and the mutated gene. (See Fig. 17 on p. 55, where '1' might refer to the wild allele, '2' to the mutant, whose lower stability would be indicated by the shorter arrow.)

On the whole, I think, Delbrück's 'model' stands the tests fairly well and we are justified in using it in further considerations.

# VI. ORDER, DISORDER AND ENTROPY

Nec corpus mentem ad cogitandum nec mens corpus ad motum, neque ad quietem nec ad aliquid (si quid est) aliud determinare potest.[26]

SPINOZA, *Ethics*, P. III, Prop. 2.

## 54. *A remarkable general conclusion from the model*

Let me refer to the last phrase in § 46, in which I tried to explain that the molecular picture of the gene made it at least conceivable 'that the miniature code should be in one-to-one correspondence with a highly complicated and specified plan of development and should somehow contain the means of putting it into operation'. Very well then, but how does it do this? How are we going to turn 'conceivability' into true understanding?

Delbrück's molecular model, in its complete generality, seems to contain no hint as to how the hereditary substance works. Indeed, I do not expect that any detailed information on this question is likely to come from physics in the near future. The advance is proceeding and will, I am sure, continue to do so, from biochemistry under the guidance of physiology and genetics.

No detailed information about the functioning of the genetical mechanism can emerge from a description of its structure so general as has been given above. That is obvious. But, strangely enough, there is just one general conclusion to be obtained from it, and that, I confess, was my only motive for writing this book.

From Delbrück's general picture of the hereditary substance it emerges that living matter, while not eluding the 'laws of physics' as established up to date, is likely to involve 'other laws of physics' hitherto unknown, which, however, once they have been revealed, will form just as integral a part of this science as the former.

[26] Neither can the body determine the mind to think, nor the mind the body to move or to rest nor to anything else, if such there be.

## 55.  *Order based on order*

This is a rather subtle line of thought, open to misconception in more than one respect. All the remaining pages are concerned with making it clear. A preliminary insight, rough but not altogether erroneous, may be found in the following considerations:

It has been explained in Section I that the laws of physics, as we know them, are statistical laws.[27] They have a lot to do with the natural tendency of things to go over into disorder.

But, to reconcile the high durability of the hereditary substance with its minute size, we had to evade the tendency to disorder by 'inventing the molecule', in fact, an unusually large molecule, which has to be a masterpiece of highly differentiated order, safeguarded by the conjuring rod of quantum theory. The laws of chance are not invalidated by this 'invention', but their outcome is modified. The physicist is familiar with the fact that the classical laws of physics are modified by quantum theory, especially at low temperature. There are many instances of this. Life seems to be one of them, a particularly striking one. Life seems to be orderly and lawful behaviour of matter, not based exclusively on its tendency to go over from order to disorder, but based partly on existing order that is kept up.

To the physicist—but only to him—I could hope to make my view clearer by saying: The living organism seems to be a macroscopic system which in part of its behaviour approaches to that purely mechanical (as contrasted with thermodynamical) conduct to which all systems tend, as the temperature approaches the absolute zero and the molecular disorder is removed.

The non-physicist finds it hard to believe that really the ordinary laws of physics, which he regards as the prototype of inviolable precision, should be based on the statistical tendency of matter to go over into disorder. I have

[27] To state this in complete generality about 'the laws of physics' is perhaps challengeable. The point will be discussed in Section VII.

given examples in Section I. The general principle involved is the famous Second Law of Thermodynamics (entropy principle) and its equally famous statistical foundation. In §§ 56–60 I will try to sketch the bearing of the entropy principle on the large-scale behaviour of a living organism—forgetting at the moment all that is known about chromosomes, inheritance, and so on.

## 56. *Living matter evades the decay to equilibrium*

What is the characteristic feature of life? When is a piece of matter said to be alive? When it goes on 'doing something', moving, exchanging material with its environment, and so forth, and that for a much longer period than we would expect an inanimate piece of matter to 'keep going' under similar circumstances. When a system that is not alive is isolated or placed in a uniform environment, all motion usually comes to a standstill very soon as a result of various kinds of friction; differences of electric or chemical potential are equalized, substances which tend to form a chemical compound do so, temperature becomes uniform by heat conduction. After that the whole system fades away into a dead, inert lump of matter. A permanent state is reached, in which no observable events occur. The physicist calls this the state of thermodynamical equilibrium, or of 'maximum entropy'.

Practically, a state of this kind is usually reached very rapidly. Theoretically, it is very often not yet an absolute equilibrium, not yet the true maximum of entropy. But then the final approach to equilibrium is very slow. It could take anything between hours, years, centuries, . . . . To give an example—one in which the approach is still fairly rapid: if a glass filled with pure water and a second one filled with sugared water are placed together in a hermetically closed case at constant temperature, it appears at first that nothing happens, and the impression of complete equilibrium is created. But after a day or so it is noticed that the pure water, owing to its higher vapour pressure, slowly evaporates and condenses on the solution.

The latter overflows. Only after the pure water has totally evaporated has the sugar reached its aim of being equally distributed among all the liquid water available.

These ultimate slow approaches to equilibrium could never be mistaken for life, and we may disregard them here. I have referred to them in order to clear myself of a charge of inaccuracy.

### 57. It feeds on 'negative entropy'

It is by avoiding the rapid decay into the inert state of 'equilibrium', that an organism appears so enigmatic; so much so, that from the earliest times of human thought some special non-physical or supernatural force (*vis viva*, entelechy) was claimed to be operative in the organism, and in some quarters is still claimed.

How does the living organism avoid decay? The obvious answer is: By eating, drinking, breathing and (in the case of plants) assimilating. The technical term is *metabolism*. The Greek word (*metabállein*) means change or exchange. Exchange of what? Originally the underlying idea is, no doubt, exchange of material. (E.g. the German for metabolism is Stoffwechsel.) That the exchange of material should be the essential thing is absured. Any atom of nitrogen, oxygen, sulphur, etc., is as good as any other of its kind; what could be gained by exchanging them? For a while in the past our curiosity was silenced by being told that we feed upon energy. In some very advanced country (I don't remember whether it was Germany or the U.S.A. or both) you could find menu cards in restaurants indicating, in addition to the price, the energy content of every dish. Needless to say, taken literally, this is just as absurd. For an adult organism the energy content is as stationary as the material content. Since, surely, any calorie is worth as much as any other calorie, one cannot see how a mere exchange could help.

What then is that precious something contained in our food which keeps us from death? That is easily answered. Every process, event, happening—call it what you will; in a word, everything that is going on in Nature means an increase of the entropy of the part of the world where it is going on. Thus a living organism continually increases its entropy—or, as you may say, produces positive entropy —and thus tends to approach the dangerous state of maximum entropy, which is death. It can only keep aloof from it, i.e. alive, by continually drawing from its environment negative entropy—which is something very positive as we shall immediately see. What an organism feeds upon is negative entropy. Or, to put it less paradoxically, the essential thing in metabolism is that the organism succeeds in freeing itself from all the entropy it cannot help producing while alive.

## 58. *What is entropy?*

What is entropy? Let me first emphasize that it is not a hazy concept or idea, but a measurable physical quantity just like the length of a rod, the temperature at any point of a body, the heat of fusion of a given crystal or the specific heat of any given substance. At the absolute zero point of temperature (roughly − 273° C.) the entropy of any substance is zero. When you bring the substance into any other state by slow, reversible little steps (even if thereby the substance changes its physical or chemical nature or splits up into two or more parts of different physical or chemical nature) the entropy increases by an amount which is computed by dividing every little portion of heat you had to supply in that procedure by the absolute temperature at which it was supplied—and by summing up all these small contributions. To give an example, when you melt a solid, its entropy increases by the amount of the heat of fusion divided by the temperature at the melting-point. You see from this, that the unit in which entropy is measured is cal./° C. (just as the calorie is the unit of heat or the centimetre the unit of length).

## 59. *The statistical meaning of entropy*

I have mentioned this technical definition simply in order to remove entropy from the atmosphere of hazy mystery

that frequently veils it. Much more important for us here
is the bearing on the statistical concept of order and disorder, a connection that was revealed by the investigations
of Boltzmann and Gibbs in statistical physics. This too is
an exact quantitative connection, and is expressed by

$$\text{entropy} = k \log D,$$

where $k$ is the so-called Boltzmann constant (= $3 \cdot 2983 \cdot$
$10^{-24}$ cal./° C.), and $D$ a quantitative measure of the
atomistic disorder of the body in question. To give an
exact explanation of this quantity $D$ in brief non-technical
terms is well-nigh impossible. The disorder it indicates is
partly that of heat motion, partly that which consists in
different kinds of atoms or molecules being mixed at
random, instead of being neatly separated, e.g. the sugar
and water molecules in the example quoted above. Boltzmann's equation is well illustrated by that example. The
gradual 'spreading out' of the sugar over all the water
available increases the disorder $D$, and hence (since the
logarithm of $D$ increases with $D$) the entropy. It is also
pretty clear that any supply of heat increases the turmoil
of heat motion, that is to say increases $D$ and thus increases the entropy; it is particularly clear that this should
be so when you melt a crystal, since you thereby destroy
the neat and permanent arrangement of the atoms or
molecules and turn the crystal lattice into a continually
changing random distribution.

An isolated system or a system in a uniform environment (which for the present consideration we do best to
include as a part of the system we contemplate) increases
its entropy and more or less rapidly approaches the inert
state of maximum entropy. We now recognize this fundamental law of physics to be just the natural tendency of
things to approach the chaotic state (the same tendency
that the books of a library or the piles of papers and
manuscripts on a writing desk display) unless we obviate
it. (The analogue of irregular heat motion, in this case, is
our handling those objects now and again without
troubling to put them back in their proper places.)

60. *Organization maintained by extracting 'order' from the environment*

How would we express in terms of the statistical theory the marvellous faculty of a living organism by which it delays the decay into thermodynamical equilibrium (death)? We said before: 'It feeds upon negative entropy', attracting, as it were, a stream of negative entropy upon itself, to compensate the entropy increase it produces by living and thus to maintain itself on a stationary and fairly low entropy level.

If *D* is a measure of disorder, its reciprocal, $1/D$, can be regarded as a direct measure of order. Since the logarithm of $1/D$ is just minus the logarithm of *D*, we can write Boltzmann's equation thus:

$$-(\text{entropy}) = k \log (1/D).$$

Hence the awkward expression 'negative entropy' can be replaced by a better one: entropy, taken with the negative sign, is itself a measure of order. Thus the device by which an organism maintains itself stationary at a fairly high level of orderliness (= fairly low level of entropy) really consists in continually sucking orderliness from its environment. This conclusion is less paradoxical than it appears at first sight. Rather could it be blamed for triviality. Indeed, in the case of higher animals we know the kind of orderliness they feed upon well enough, viz. the extremely well-ordered state of matter in more or less complicated organic compounds, which serve them as foodstuffs. After utilizing it they return it in a very much degraded form—not entirely degraded, however, for plants can still make use of it. (These, of course, have their most powerful supply of 'negative entropy' in the sunlight.)

See note to Section VI, p. 83.

# VII.   IS LIFE BASED ON THE LAWS OF PHYSICS?

> Si un hombre nunca se contradice, será porque
> nunca dice nada.[28]        MIGUEL DE UNAMUNO
>                              (quoted from conversation)

### 61.  *New laws to be expected in the organism*

What I wish to make clear in this last chapter is, in short,
that from all we have learnt about the structure of living
matter, we must be prepared to find it working in a manner that cannot be reduced to the ordinary laws of physics.
And that not on the ground that there is any 'new force'
or what not, directing the behaviour of the single atoms
within a living organism, but because the construction is
different from anything we have yet tested in the physical
laboratory. To put it crudely, an engineer familiar with
heat engines only will, after inspecting the construction
of an electric motor, be prepared to find it working along
principles which he does not yet understand. He finds the
copper familiar to him in kettles used here in the form of
long, long wires wound in coils; the iron familiar to him
in levers and bars and steam cylinders is here filling the
interior of those coils of copper wire. He will be convinced
that it is the same copper and the same iron, subject to
the same laws of Nature, and he is right in that. The
difference in construction is enough to prepare him for an
entirely different way of functioning. He will not suspect
that an electric motor is driven by a ghost because it is
set spinning by the turn of a switch, without boiler and
steam.

### 62.  *Reviewing the biological situation*

The unfolding of events in the life cycle of an organism
exhibits an admirable regularity and orderliness, unrivalled
by anything we meet with in inanimate matter. We find it

[28] If a man never contradicts himself, the reason must be that
he virtually never says anything at all.

controlled by a supremely well-ordered group of atoms, which represent only a very small fraction of the sum total in every cell. Moreover, from the view we have formed of the mechanism of mutation we conclude that the dislocation of just a few atoms within the group of 'governing atoms' of the germ cell suffices to bring about a well-defined change in the large-scale hereditary characteristics of the organism.

These facts are easily the most interesting that science has revealed in our day. We may be inclined to find them, after all, not wholly unacceptable. An organism's astonishing gift of concentrating a 'stream of order' on itself and thus escaping the decay into atomic chaos—of 'drinking orderliness' from a suitable environment—seems to be connected with the presence of the 'aperiodic solids', the chromosome molecules, which doubtless represent the highest degree of well-ordered atomic association we know of—much higher than the ordinary periodic crystal—in virtue of the individual role every atom and every radical is playing here.

To put it briefly, we witness the event that existing order displays the power of maintaining itself and of producing orderly events. That sounds plausible enough, though in finding it plausible we, no doubt, draw on experience concerning social organization and other events which involve the activity of organisms. And so it might seem that something like a vicious circle is implied.

### 63. *Summarizing the physical situation*

However that may be, the point to emphasize again and again is that to the physicist the state of affairs is not only not plausible but most exciting, because it is unprecedented. Contrary to the common belief, the regular course of events, governed by the laws of physics, is never the consequence of one well-ordered configuration of atoms—not unless that configuration of atoms repeats itself a great number of times, either as in the periodic crystal or as in a liquid or in a gas composed of a great number of identical molecules.

Even when the chemist handles a very complicated molecule *in vitro* he is always faced with an enormous number of like molecules. To them his laws apply. He might tell you, for example, that one minute after he has started some particular reaction half of the molecules will have reacted, and after a second minute three-quarters of them will have done so. But whether any particular molecule, supposing you could follow its course, will be among those which have reacted or among those which are still untouched, he could not predict. That is a matter of pure chance.

This is not a purely theoretical conjecture. It is not that we can never observe the fate of a single small group of atoms or even of a single atom. We can, occasionally. But whenever we do, we find complete irregularity, co-operating to produce regularity only on the average. We have dealt with an example in Section I. The Brownian movement of a small particle suspended in a liquid is completely irregular. But if there are many similar particles, they will by their irregular movement give rise to the regular phenomenon of diffusion.

The disintegration of a single radioactive atom is observable (it emits a projectile which causes a visible scintillation on a fluorescent screen). But if you are given a single radioactive atom, its probable lifetime is much less certain than that of a healthy sparrow. Indeed, nothing more can be said about it than this: as long as it lives (and that may be for thousands of years) the chance of its blowing up within the next second, whether large or small, remains the same. This patent lack of individual determination nevertheless results in the exact exponential law of decay of a large number of radioactive atoms of the same kind.

## 64. *The striking contrast*

In biology we are faced with an entirely different situation. A single group of atoms existing only in one copy produces orderly events, marvellously tuned in with each other and with the environment according to most subtle laws. I said, existing only in one copy, for after all we have the example of the egg and of the unicellular organism. In the following stages of a higher organism the copies are multiplied, that is true. But to what extent? Something like $10^{14}$ in a grown mammal, I understand. What is that! Only a millionth of the number of molecules in one cubic inch of air. Though comparatively bulky, by coalescing they would form but a tiny drop of liquid. And look at the way they are actually distributed. Every cell harbours just one of them (or two, if we bear in mind diploidy). Since we know the power this tiny central office has in the isolated cell, do they not resemble stations of local government dispersed through the body, communicating with each other with great ease, thanks to the code that is common to all of them?

Well, this is a fantastic description, perhaps less becoming a scientist than a poet. However, it needs no poetical imagination but only clear and sober scientific reflection to recognize that we are here obviously faced with events whose regular and lawful unfolding is guided by a 'mechanism' entirely different from the 'probability mechanism' of physics. For it is simply a fact of observation that the guiding principle in every cell is embodied in a single atomic association existing only in one copy (or sometimes two)—and a fact of observation that it results in producing events which are a paragon of orderliness. Whether we find it astonishing or whether we find it quite plausible, that a small but highly organized group of atoms be capable of acting in this manner, the situation is unprecedented, it is unknown anywhere else except in living matter. The physicist and the chemist, investigating inanimate matter, have never witnessed phenomena which they had to interpret in this way. The case did not arise and so our theory does not cover it—our beautiful statistical theory of which we were so justly proud because it allowed us to look behind the curtain, to watch the magnificent order of exact physical law coming forth from atomic and molecular disorder; because it revealed that the most important, the most general, the all-embracing, law of entropy increase could be understood without a special assumption *ad hoc*, for it is nothing but molecular disorder itself.

### 65.  *Two ways of producing orderliness*

The orderliness encountered in the unfolding of life springs from a different source. It appears that there are two different 'mechanisms' by which orderly events can be produced: the 'statistical mechanism' which produces 'order from disorder' and the new one, producing 'order from order'. To the unprejudiced mind the second principle appears to be much simpler, much more plausible. No doubt it is. That is why physicists were so proud to have fallen in with the other one, the 'order-from-disorder' principle, which is actually followed in Nature and which alone conveys an understanding of the great line of natural events, in the first place of their irreversibility. But we cannot expect that the 'laws of physics' derived from it suffice straightaway to explain the behaviour of living matter, whose most striking features are visibly based to a large extent on the 'order-from-order' principle. You would not expect two entirely different mechanisms to bring about the same type of law—you would not expect your latch-key to open your neighbour's door as well.

We must therefore not be discouraged by the difficulty of interpreting life by the ordinary laws of physics. For that is just what is to be expected from the knowledge we have gained of the structure of living matter. We must be prepared to find a new type of physical law prevailing in it. Or are we to term it a non-physical, not to say a super-physical, law?

### 66.  *The new principle is not alien to physics*

No. I do not think that. For the new principle that is involved is a genuinely physical one: it is, in my opinion, nothing else than the principle of quantum theory over again. To explain this, we have to go to some length, including a refinement, not to say an amendment, of the assertion previously made, namely, that all physical laws are based on statistics.

This assertion, made again and again, could not fail to arouse contradiction. For, indeed, there are phenomena whose conspicuous features are visibly based directly on the 'order-from-order' principle and appear to have nothing to do with statistics or molecular disorder.

The order of the solar system, the motion of the planets, is maintained for an almost indefinite time. The constellation of this moment is directly connected with the constellation at any particular moment in the times of the Pyramids; it can be traced back to it, or vice versa. Historical eclipses have been calculated and have been found in close agreement with historical records or have even in some cases served to correct the accepted chronology. These calculations do not imply any statistics, they are based solely on Newton's law of universal attraction.

Nor does the regular motion of a good clock or of any similar mechanism appear to have anything to do with statistics. In short, all purely mechanical events seem to follow distinctly and directly the 'order-from-order' principle. And if we say 'mechanical', the term must be taken in a wide sense. A very useful kind of clock is, as you know, based on the regular transmission of electric pulses from the power station.

I remember an interesting little paper by Max Planck on the topic 'The Dynamical and the Statistical Type of Law' ('Dynamische und Statistische Gesetzmässigkeit'). The distinction is precisely the one we have here labelled as 'order from order' and 'order from disorder'. The object of that paper was to show how the interesting statistical type of law, controlling large-scale events, is constituted from the 'dynamical' laws supposed to govern the small-scale events, the interaction of the single atoms and molecules. The latter type is illustrated by large-scale mechanical phenomena, as the motion of the planets or of a clock, etc.

Thus it would appear that the 'new principle', the order-from-order principle, to which we have pointed with great solemnity as being the real clue to the understanding of life, is not at all new to physics. Planck's attitude even vindicates priority for it. We seem to arrive at the ridiculous conclusion that the clue to the understanding of life is that it is based on a pure mechanism, a 'clock-work' in the sense of Planck's paper. The conclusion is not ridiculous and is, in my opinion, not entirely wrong, but it has to be taken 'with a very big grain of salt'

### 67. *The motion of a clock*

Let us analyse the motion of a real clock accurately. It is not at all a purely mechanical phenomenon. A purely mechanical clock would need no spring, no winding. Once set in motion, it would go on for ever. A real clock without a spring stops after a few beats of the pendulum, its mechanical energy is turned into heat. This is an infinitely complicated atomistic process. The general picture the physicist forms of it compels him to admit that the inverse process is not entirely impossible: A springless clock might suddenly begin to move, at the expense of the heat energy of its own cog wheels and of the environment. The physicist would have to say: The clock experiences an exceptionally intense fit of Brownian movement. We have seen in Section I (§ 9) that with a very sensitive torsional balance (electrometer or galvanometer) that sort of thing happens all the time. In the case of a clock it is, of course, infinitely unlikely.

Whether the motion of a clock is to be assigned to the dynamical or to the statistical type of lawful events (to use Planck's expressions) depends on our attitude. In calling it a dynamical phenomenon we fix attention on the regular going that can be secured by a comparatively weak spring, which overcomes the small disturbances by heat motion, so that we may disregard them. But if we remember that without a spring the clock is gradually slowed down by friction, we find that this process can only be understood as a statistical phenomenon.

However insignificant the frictional and heating effects in a clock may be from the practical point of view, there can be no doubt that the second attitude, which does not neglect them, is the more fundamental one, even when we are faced with the regular motion of a clock that is driven by a spring. For it must not be believed that the driving mechanism really does away with the statistical nature of the process. The true physical picture includes the possibility that even a regularly going clock should all at once invert its motion and, working backward, rewind its own spring—at the expense of the heat of the environment. The event is just 'still a little less likely' than a 'Brownian fit' of a clock without driving mechanism.

## 68. *Clockwork after all statistical*

Let us now review the situation. The 'simple' case we have analysed is representative of many others—in fact of all such as appear to evade the all-embracing principle of molecular statistics. Clock-works made of real physical matter (in contrast to imagination) are not true 'clock-works'. The element of chance may be more or less reduced, the likelihood of the clock suddenly going altogether wrong may be infinitesimal, but it always remains in the background. Even in the motion of the celestial bodies irreversible fractional and thermal influences are not wanting. Thus the rotation of the earth is slowly diminished by tidal friction, and along with this reduction the moon gradually recedes from the earth, which would not happen if the earth were a completely rigid rotating sphere.

Nevertheless the fact remains that 'physical clock-works' visibly display very prominent 'order-from-order' features —the type that aroused the physicist's excitement when he encountered them in the organism. It seems likely that the two cases have after all something in common. It remains to be seen what this is and what is the striking difference which makes the case of the organism after all novel and unprecedented.

## 69. *Nernst's Theorem*

When does a physical system—any kind of association of atoms—display 'dynamical law' (in Planck's meaning) or 'clock-work features'? Quantum theory has a very short answer to this question, viz. at the absolute zero of temperature. As zero temperature is approached the molecular disorder ceases to have any bearing on physical events. This fact was, by the way, not discovered by theory, but by carefully investigating chemical reactions over a wide range of temperatures and extrapolating the results to zero temperature—which cannot actually be reached. This is Walther Nernst's famous 'Heat-Theorem', which is sometimes, and not unduly, given the proud name of the 'Third Law of Thermodynamics' (the first being the energy principle, the second the entropy principle).

Quantum theory provides the rational foundation of Nernst's empirical law, and also enables us to estimate how closely a system must approach to the absolute zero in order to display an approximately 'dynamical' behaviour. What temperature is in any particular case already practically equivalent to zero?

Now you must not believe that this always has to be a very low temperature. Indeed, Nernst's discovery was induced by the fact that even at room temperature entropy plays an astonishingly insignificant role in many chemical reactions. (Let me recall that entropy is a direct measure of molecular disorder, viz. its logarithm.)

## 70. *The pendulum clock is virtually at zero temperature*

What about a pendulum clock? For a pendulum clock room temperature is practically equivalent to zero. That is the reason why it works 'dynamically'. It will continue to work as it does if you cool it (provided that you have removed all traces of oil!). But it does not continue to work if you heat it above room temperature, for it will eventually melt.

## 71. *The relation between clock-work and organism*

That seems very trivial but it does, I think, hit the cardinal point. Clock-works are capable of functioning 'dynamically' because they are built of solids, which are kept in shape by London-Heitler forces, strong enough to elude the disorderly tendency of heat motion at ordinary temperature.

Now, I think, few words more are needed to disclose the point of resemblance between a clock-work and an organism. It is simply and solely that the latter also hinges upon a solid—the aperiodic crystal forming the hereditary substance, largely withdrawn from the disorder of heat motion. But please do not accuse me of calling the chromosome fibres just the 'cogs of the organic machine'— at least not without a reference to the profound physical theories on which the simile is based.

For, indeed, it needs still less rhetoric to recall the fundamental difference between the two and to justify the epithets novel and unprecedented in the biological case.

The most striking features are: first, the curious distribution of the cogs in a many-celled organism, for which I may refer to the somewhat poetical description in § 64; and secondly, the fact that the single cog is not of coarse human make, but is the finest masterpiece ever achieved along the lines of the Lord's quantum mechanics.

### NOTES TO SECTION VI

The remarks on *negative entropy* have met with doubt and opposition from physicist colleagues. Let me say first, that if I had been catering for them alone I should have let the discussion turn on *free energy* instead. It is the more familiar notion in this context. But this highly technical term seemed linguistically too near to *energy* for making the average reader alive to the contrast between the two things. He is likely to take *free* as more or less an *epitheton ornans* without much relevance, while actually the concept is a rather intricate one, whose relation to Boltzmann's order-disorder principle is less easy to trace than for entropy and 'entropy taken with a negative sign', which by the way is not my invention. It happens to be precisely the thing on which Boltzmann's original argument turned.

But F. Simon has very pertinently pointed out to me that my simple thermodynamical considerations cannot account for our having to feed on matter 'in the extremely well-ordered state of more or less complicated organic compounds' rather than on charcoal or diamond pulp. He is right. But to the lay reader I must explain that a piece of unburnt coal or diamond, together with the amount of oxygen needed for its combustion, is also in an extremely well-ordered state, as the physicist understands it.

Witness to this: if you allow the reaction, the burning of the coal, to take place, a great amount of heat is produced. By giving it off to the surroundings, the system disposes of the very considerable entropy increase entailed by the reaction, and reaches a state in which it has, in point of fact, roughly the same entropy as before.

Yet we could not feed on the carbon dioxide that results from the reaction. And so Simon is quite right in pointing out to me, as he did, that actually the energy content of our food *does* matter; so my mocking at the menu cards that indicate it was out of place. Energy is needed to replace not only the mechanical energy of our bodily exertions, but also the heat we continually give off to the environment. And that we give off heat is not accidental, but essential. For this is precisely the manner in which we dispose of the surplus entropy we continually produce in our physical life process.

*yes* ✓

This seems to suggest that the higher temperature of the warm-blooded animal includes the advantage of enabling it to get rid of its entropy at a quicker rate, so that it can afford a more intense life process. I am not sure how much truth there is in this argument (for which I am responsible, not Simon). One may hold against it, that on the other hand many warm-blooders are *protected* against the rapid loss of heat by coats of fur or feathers. So the parallelism between body temperature and 'intensity of life', which I believe to exist, may have to be accounted for more directly by van 't Hoff's law, mentioned at the end of § 50: the higher temperature itself speeds up the chemical reactions involved in living. (That it actually does, has been confirmed experimentally in species which take the temperature of the surrounding.)

## EPILOGUE: ON DETERMINISM AND FREE WILL

As a reward for the serious trouble I have taken to expound the purely scientific aspect of our problem *sine ira et studio*, I beg leave to add my own, necessarily subjective, view of its philosophical implications.

According to the evidence put forward in the preceding pages the space-time events in the body of a living being which correspond to the activity of its mind, to its self-conscious or any other actions, are (considering also their complex structure and the accepted statistical explanation of physico-chemistry) if not strictly deterministic at any rate statistico-deterministic. To the physicist I wish to emphasize that in my opinion, and contrary to the opinion upheld in some quarters, *quantum indeterminacy* plays no biologically relevant role in them, except perhaps by enhancing their purely accidental character in such events as meiosis, natural and X-ray-induced mutation, and so on —and this is in any case obvious and well recognized.

For the sake of argument, let me regard this as a fact, as I believe every unbiassed biologist would, if there were not the well-known, unpleasant feeling about 'declaring oneself to be a pure mechanism'. For it is deemed to contradict Free Will as warranted by direct introspection.

But immediate experiences in themselves, however various and disparate they be, are logically incapable of contradicting each other. So let us see whether we cannot draw the correct, non-contradictory conclusion from the following two premises:

(i) My body functions as a pure mechanism according to the Laws of Nature.

(ii) Yet I know, by incontrovertible direct experience, that I am directing its motions, of which I foresee the effects, that may be fateful and all-important, in which case I feel and take full responsibility for them.

The only possible inference from these two facts is, I think, that I—I in the widest meaning of the word, that is to say, every conscious mind that has ever said or felt 'I'— am the person, if any, who controls the 'motion of the atoms' according to the Laws of Nature.

Within a cultural milieu (Kulturkreis) where certain conceptions (which once had or still have a wider meaning amongst other peoples) have been limited and specialized, it is daring to give to this conclusion the simple wording that it requires. In Christian terminology to say: 'Hence I am God Almighty' sounds both blasphemous and lunatic. But please disregard these connotations for the moment and consider whether the above inference is not the closest a biologist can get to proving God and immortality at one stroke.

In itself, the insight is not new. The earliest records to my knowledge date back some 2500 years or more. From the early great Upanishads the recognition ATHMAN = BRAHMAN (the personal self equals the omnipresent, all-comprehending eternal self) was in Indian thought considered, far from being blasphemous, to represent the quintessence of deepest insight into the happenings of the world. The striving of all the scholars of Vedanta was, after having learnt to pronounce with their lips, really to assimilate in their minds this grandest of all thoughts.

Again, the mystics of many centuries, independently, yet in perfect harmony with each other (somewhat like the particles in an ideal gas) have described, each of them, the unique experience of his or her life in terms that can be condensed in the phrase: DEUS FACTUS SUM (I have become God).

To Western ideology the thought has remained a stranger, in spite of Schopenhauer and others who stood for it, and in spite of those true lovers who, as they look into each other's eyes, become aware that their thought and their joy are *numerically* one—not merely similar or identical; but they, as a rule, are emotionally too busy to indulge in clear thinking, in which respect they very much resemble the mystic.

Allow me a few further comments. Consciousness is never experienced in the plural, only in the singular. Even in the pathological cases of split consciousness or double personality the two persons alternate, they are never manifest simultaneously. In a dream we do perform several characters at the same time, but not indiscriminately: we *are* one of them; in him we act and speak directly, while we often eagerly await the answer or response of another person, unaware of the fact that it is we who control his movements and his speech just as much as our own.

How does the idea of plurality (so emphatically opposed by the Upanishad writers) arise at all? Consciousness finds itself intimately connected with, and dependent on, the physical state of a limited region of matter, the body. (Consider the changes of mind during the development of the body, as puberty, ageing, dotage, etc., or consider the effects of fever, intoxication, narcosis, lesion of the brain, and so on.) Now, there is a great plurality of similar bodies. Hence the pluralization of consciousnesses or minds seems a very suggestive hypothesis. Probably all simple ingenious people, as well as the great majority of Western philosophers, have accepted it.

It leads almost immediately to the invention of souls, as many as there are bodies, and to the question whether they are mortal as the body is or whether they are immortal and capable of existing by themselves. The former alternative is distasteful, while the latter frankly forgets, ignores, or disowns the facts upon which the plurality hypothesis rests. Much sillier questions have been asked: Do animals also have souls? It has even been questioned whether women, or only men, have souls.

Such consequences, even if only tentative, must make us suspicious of the plurality hypothesis, which is common to all official Western creeds. Are we not inclining to much greater nonsense, if in discarding their gross superstitions we retain their naïve idea of plurality of souls, but 'remedy' it by declaring the souls to be perishable, to be annihilated with the respective bodies?

The only possible alternative is simply to keep to the immediate experience that consciousness is a singular of which the plural is unknown; that there *is* only one thing and that what seems to be a plurality is merely a series of different aspects of this one thing, produced by a deception (the Indian MAJA); the same illusion is produced in a gallery of mirrors, and in the same way Gaurisankar and Mt. Everest turned out to be the same peak seen from different valleys.

There are, of course, elaborate ghost-stories fixed in our minds to hamper our acceptance of such simple recognition. E.g. it has been said that there is a tree there outside my window, but I do not really see the tree. By some cunning device of which only the initial, relatively simple, steps are explored, the real tree throws an image of itself into my consciousness, and that is what I perceive. If you stand by my side and look at the same tree, the latter manages to throw an image into your soul as well. I see my tree and you see yours (remarkably like mine), and what the tree in itself is we do not know. For this extravagance Kant is responsible. In the order of ideas which regards consciousness as a *singulare tantum* it is conveniently replaced by the statement that there is obviously only *one* tree and all the image business is a ghost-story.

Yet each of us has the undisputable impression that the sum total of his own experience and memory forms a unit, quite distinct from that of any other person. He refers to it as 'I'. *What is this 'I'?*

If you analyse it closely you will, I think, find that it is just a little bit more than a collection of single data (experiences and memories), namely the canvas *upon which* they are collected. And you will, on close introspection, find that what you really mean by 'I' is that ground-stuff upon which they are collected. You may come to a distant country, lose sight of all your friends, may all but forget them; you acquire new friends, you share life with them as intensely as you ever did with your old ones. Less and less important will become the fact that, while living your new life, you still recollect the old one. 'The youth that was I', you may come to speak of him in the third person, indeed the protagonist of the novel you are reading is probably nearer to your heart, certainly more intensely alive and better known to you. Yet there has been no intermediate break, no death. And even if a skilled hypnotist succeeded in blotting out entirely all your earlier reminiscences, you would not find that he had killed *you*. In no case is there a loss of personal existence to deplore.

Nor will there ever be.

### NOTE TO THE EPILOGUE

The point of view taken here levels with what *Aldous Huxley* has recently—and very appropriately—called *Perennial Philosophy*. His beautiful book (New York, Harper & Bros. 1945, and London, Chatto & Windus 1946) is singularly fit to explain not only the state of affairs, but also why it is so difficult to grasp and so liable to meet with opposition.

# Nature and the Greeks

## I. THE MOTIVES FOR RETURNING
## TO ANCIENT THOUGHT

When, early in 1948, I set out to deliver a course of public
lectures on the subject dealt with here, I still felt the
urgent need of prefacing them with ample explanations
and excuses. What I was expounding then and there (to
wit, at University College, Dublin) has come to form a
part of the little book before you. Some comment from
the standpoint of modern science was added, and a brief
exposition of what I deem to be the peculiar fundamental
features of the present-day scientific world-picture. To
prove that these features are historically produced (as
against logically necessitated), by tracing them back to
the earliest stage of Western philosophic thought, was my
real objective in enlarging on the latter. Yet, as I said, I
did feel a little uneasy, particularly since those lectures
arose from my official duty as a professor of theoretical
physics. There was need to explain (though I was myself
not so thoroughly convinced of it) that in passing the
time with narratives about ancient Greek thinkers and
with comments on their views I was *not* just following a
recently acquired hobby of mine; that it did not mean,
from the professional point of view, a waste of time, which
ought to be relegated to the hours of leisure; that it was

* Section I is the first chapter of *Nature and the Greeks* (Cambridge: Cambridge University Press, 1954), pp. 1–19.

justified by the hope of some gain in understanding modern science and thus *inter alia* also modern physics.

A few months later, in May, when speaking on the same topic at University College, London (Shearman Lectures, 1948), I already felt much more self-assured. While I had initially found myself supported mainly by such eminent scholars of antiquity as Theodor Gomperz, John Burnet, Cyril Bailey, Benjamin Farrington—some of whose pregnant remarks will later be quoted—I very soon became aware that it was probably neither haphazard nor personal predilection which made me plunge into the history of thought some twenty centuries deeper than other scientists had been induced to sound, who responded to the example and the exhortation of Ernst Mach. Far from following an odd impulse of my own, I had been swept along unwittingly, as happens so often, by a trend of thought rooted somehow in the intellectual situation of our time. Indeed, within the short period of one or two years several books had been published, whose authors were not classical scholars but were primarily interested in the scientific and philosophic thought of today; yet they had devoted a very substantial part of the scholarly labour embodied in their books to expounding and scrutinizing the earliest roots of modern thought in ancient writings. There is the posthumous *Growth of Physical Science* by the late Sir James Jeans, eminent astronomer and physicist, widely known to the public by his brilliant and successful popularizations. There is the marvellous *History of Western Philosophy* by Bertrand Russell, on whose manifold merits I need not and cannot enlarge here; I only wish to recall that Bertrand Russell entered his brilliant career as the philosopher of modern mathematics and mathematical logic. About one third of each of these volumes is concerned with antiquity. A handsome volume of a similar scope, entitled *The Birth of Science* (*Die Geburt der Wissenschaft*) was sent to me at nearly the same time from Innsbruck by the author, Anton von Mörl, who is neither a scholar of antiquity, nor of science, nor of philosophy; he had the misfortune at the time when Hitler marched into Austria to be the Chief of Police

(*Sicherheitsdirector*) of Tirol, a crime for which he had to suffer many years in a concentration camp; he luckily survived the ordeal.

Now if I am right in calling this a general trend of our time, the questions naturally arise: how did it originate, what were its causes, and what does it really mean? Such questions can hardly ever be answered exhaustively even when the trend of thought that we consider lies far enough back in history for us to have gained a fair survey of the total human situation of the time. In dealing with a quite recent development one can at best hope to point out one or another of the contributory facts or features. In the present case there are, I believe, two circumstances that may serve as a partial explanation of the strongly retrospective tendency among those concerned with the history of ideas: *one* refers to the intellectual and emotional phase mankind in general has entered in our days, the *other* is the inordinately critical situation in which nearly all the fundamental sciences find themselves ever more disconcertingly enveloped (as against their highly flourishing offspring like engineering, practical—including nuclear—chemistry, medical and surgical art and technique). Let me briefly explain these two points, beginning with the first.

As Bertrand Russell has recently[1] pointed out with particular clarity, the growing antagonism between religion and science did not arise from accidental circumstances, nor is it, generally speaking, caused by ill will on either side. A considerable amount of mutual distrust is, alas, natural and understandable. One of the aims, if not perhaps the main task, of religious movements has always been to round off the ever unaccomplished understanding of the unsatisfactory and bewildering situation in which man finds himself in the world; to *close* the disconcerting 'openness' of the outlook gained from experience alone, in order to raise his confidence in life and strengthen his natural benevolence and sympathy towards his fellow creatures—innate properties, so I believe, but easily overpowered by personal mishaps and the pangs of misery.

[1] *Hist. West. Phil.* p. 559.

Now, in order to satisfy the ordinary, unlearned man, this rounding-off of the fragmentary and incoherent world picture has to furnish *inter alia* an explanation of all those traits of the material world that are either really not yet understood at the time or not in a way the ordinary unlearned man can grasp. This need is seldom overlooked for the simple reason that, as a rule, it is shared by the person or persons who, by their eminent characters, their sociable inclination, and their deeper insight into human affairs, have the power to prevail on the masses and to fill them with enthusiasm for their enlightened moral teaching. It so happens that such persons, as regards their upbringing and learning and apart from these extraordinary qualities, have usually themselves been quite ordinary men. Their views about the material universe would thus be as precarious, actually much the same, as those of their listeners. Anyhow, they would consider the spreading of the latest news about it irrelevant for their purpose, even if they knew them.

At first this mattered little or nothing. But in the course of the centuries, particularly after the rebirth of science in the seventeenth century, it came to matter a lot. According as, on the one hand, the teachings of religion were codified and petrified and, on the other hand, science came to transform—not to say disfigure—the life of the day beyond recognition and thereby to intrude into the mind of every man, the mutual distrust between religion and science was bound to grow up. It did not spring from those well-known irrelevant details from which it ostensibly issued, such as whether the earth is in motion or at rest, or whether or not man is a late descendant of the animal kingdom; such bones of contention can be overcome, and to a large extent have been overcome. The misgiving is much more deeply rooted. By explaining more and more about the material structure of the world, and about how our environment and our bodily selves had, by natural causes, reached the state in which we find them, moreover by giving this knowledge away to everybody who was interested, the scientific outlook, so it was feared, stealthily wrested more and more from the hands of the Godhead, heading thus for a *self-contained* world to which God was in danger of becoming a gratuitous embellishment. It would hardly do justice to those who genuinely harboured this fear, if we declared it utterly unfounded. Socially and morally dangerous misgivings may spring, and occasionally have sprung—not, of course, from people knowing too much—but from people believing that they know a good deal more than they do.

Equally justified is, however, an apprehension which is, so to say, complementary, and which has haunted science from the very time it came into existence. Science has to be careful of incompetent interference from the other side, particularly in scientific disguise, recalling Mephisto, who, in the borrowed robe of the Doctor, foists his irreverent jokes upon the ingenuous Scholar. What I mean is this. In an honest search for knowledge you quite often have to abide by ignorance for an indefinite period. Instead of filling a gap by guesswork, genuine science prefers to put up with it; and this, not so much from conscientious scruples about telling lies, as from the consideration that, however irksome the gap may be, its obliteration by a fake removes the urge to seek after a tenable answer. So efficiently may attention be diverted that the answer is missed even when, by good luck, it comes close at hand. The steadfastness in standing up to a *non liquet,* nay in appreciating it as a stimulus and a signpost to further quest, is a natural and indispensable disposition in the mind of a scientist. This in itself is apt to set him at variance with the religious aim of closing the picture, unless each of the two antagonistic attitudes, both legitimate for their respective purposes, is applied with prudence.

Such gaps easily evoke the impression of being undefended weak spots. They are at times seized upon by persons whom they please, not as an incentive for further quest, but as an antidote against their fear that science might, by 'explaining everything', deprive the world of its metaphysical interest. A new hypothesis is put up, as everybody is, of course, entitled to do in such a case. At first sight it seems firmly anchored in obvious facts; one only wonders why these facts or the ease with which the proposed explanation follows from them have escaped everybody else. But this in itself is no objection, for it is precisely the situation we very often have to face in the case of genuine discoveries. However, on closer inspection the enterprise betrays its character (in the cases I have in mind) by the fact that, while apparently tendering an acceptable explanation within a fairly wide range of inquiry, it is at variance with generally established principles of sound science, which it either pretends to overlook or airily reduces with regard to their generality; to believe in the latter, so we are told, was just the prejudice that was in the way of a correct interpretation of the phenomena in question. But the creative vigour of a general principle depends precisely on its generality. By losing ground it loses all its strength and can no longer serve as a reliable guide, because in every single instance of application its competence may be challenged. To clinch the suspicion that this dethronement was not an accidental by-product of the whole enterprise, but its sinister goal, the territory from which previous scientific attainment is invited to retire is with admirable dexterity claimed as a playground of some religious ideology that cannot really use it profitably, because its true domain is far beyond anything in reach of scientific explanation.

A well-known instance of such intrusion is the recurring attempt to reintroduce *finality* into science, allegedly because the reiterated crisis of *causality* prove it to be incompetent single-handed, actually because it is considered *infra dig.* of God Almighty to create a world which He disallowed Himself to tamper with ever after. In this case the weak spots seized upon are obvious. Neither in the theory of evolution nor in the mind-matter problem has science been able to adumbrate the causal linkage satisfactorily even to its most ardent disciples. And so *vis viva,* *élan vital,* entelechy, wholeness, directed mutations, quantum mechanics of free will, etc. stepped in. As a curiosity, let me mention a neat volume[2] printed on much better

---

[2] Zeno Bucher, *Die Innenwelt der Atome* (Lucerne: Josef Stocker, 1946).

paper and in much more handsome form than British authors were used to at that time. After a sound and scholarly report on modern physics, the author happily embarks on the teleology, the purposiveness, of the interior of the atom and interprets in this manner all its activities, the movements of the electrons, the emission and absorption of radiation, etc.,

> And hopes to please by this peculiar whim
> The God who fashioned it and gave it him.[3]

But let me return to our general topic. I was trying to set forth the intrinsic causes for the natural enmity between science and religion. The fights that sprang from it in the past are too well known to call for further comment. Moreover, they are not what concerns us here. However deplorable, they still manifested mutual interest. Scientists on the one side, and metaphysicians, both of the official and of the learned type, on the other, were still aware that their endeavours to secure insight referred after all to the same object—man and his world. A clearance of the widely diverging opinions was still felt a necessity. It has not been attained. The comparative truce we witness today, at least among cultured people, was not reached by setting in harmony with one another the two kinds of outlook, the strictly scientific and the metaphysical, but rather by a resolve to ignore each other, little short of contempt. In a treatise on physics or biology, albeit a popular one, to digress to the metaphysical aspect of the subject is considered impertinent, and if a scientist dare, he is liable to have his fingers rapped and be left to guess whether it is for offending science or the particular brand of metaphysics to which the critic is devoted. It is pathetically amusing to observe how on the one side only scientific information is taken seriously, while the other side ranges science among man's worldly activities, whose findings are less momentous and have, as a matter of course, to give way when at variance with the superior insight gained in a different fashion, by pure thought or by revelation. One regrets to see mankind strive towards the same

[3] From Kenneth Hare, *The Puritan.*

goal along two different and difficult winding paths, with blinkers and separating walls, and with little attempt to join all forces and to achieve, if not a full understanding of nature and the human situation, at least the soothing recognition of the intrinsic unity of our search. This is regrettable, I say, and would be a sad spectacle anyhow, because it obviously reduces the range of what could be attained if all the thinking power at our disposal were pooled without bias. However, the loss might perhaps be endured if the metaphor I used were really appropriate, that is to say, if it were actually two different crowds who follow two paths. But this is not so. Many of us are not decided which one to follow. With regret, nay with despair, many find that they have to shut themselves off alternately from the one and from the other kind of outlook. It is certainly not in general the case that by acquiring a good all-round scientific education you so completely satisfy the innate longing for a religious or philosophical stabilization, in face of the vicissitudes of everyday life, as to feel quite happy without anything more. What does happen often is that science suffices to jeopardize popular religious convictions, but not to replace them by anything else. This produces the grotesque phenomenon of scientifically trained, highly competent minds with an unbelievably childlike—undeveloped or atrophied—philosophical outlook.

If you live in fairly comfortable and secure conditions, and take them to be human life's general pattern, which, thanks to inevitable progress, wherein you believe, is about to spread and to become universal, you seem to get along quite well without any philosophical outlook; if not indefinitely, at least until you grow old and decrepit and begin to face death as a reality. But while the early stages of the rapid material advancement which came in the wake of modern science appeared to inaugurate an era of peace, security and progress, this state of affairs now no longer prevails. Matters have sadly changed. Many people, indeed entire populations, have been thrown out of their comfort and safety, have suffered inordinate bereavements, and look into a dim future for themselves and for those of their children who have not perished. The very survival, let alone the continued progress, of man is no longer regarded as certain. Personal misery, buried hopes, impending disaster, and distrust of the prudence and honesty of the worldly rulers are apt to make men crave for even a vague hope, whether rigorously provable or not, that the 'world' or 'life' of experience be embedded in a context of higher, if as yet inscrutable, significance. But there is the wall, separating the 'two paths', that of the heart and that of pure reason. We look back along the wall: could we not pull it down, has it always been there? As we scan its windings over hills and vales back in history we behold a land far, far, away at a space of over two thousand years back, where the wall flattens and disappears and the path was not yet split, but was only *one*. Some of us deem it worth while to walk back and see what can be learnt from the alluring primeval unity.

Dropping the metaphor, it is my opinion that the philosophy of the ancient Greeks attracts us at this moment, because never before or since, anywhere in the world, has anything like their highly advanced and articulated system of knowledge and speculation been established *without* the fateful division which has hampered us for centuries and has become unendurable in our days. There were, of course, widely diverging opinions, combating one another with no less fervour, and occasionally with no more honourable means—such as unacknowledged borrowing and destruction of writings—than elsewhere and at other periods. But there was no limitation as to the subjects on which a learned man would be allowed by other learned men to give his opinion. It was still agreed that the true subject was essentially one, and that important conclusions reached about any part of it could, and as a rule would, bear on almost every other part. The idea of delimitation in water-tight compartments had not yet sprung up. A man could easily find himself blamed, conversely, for shutting his eyes to such interconnexion—as were the early atomists for being silent on the consequences in ethics of the universal necessity which they assumed, and for failing to explain how the motions of the atoms and those observed in the skies had originally been set up. To put it dramatically: one can imagine a scholar of the young School of Athens paying a holiday visit to Abdera (with due caution to keep it secret from his Master), and on being received by the wise, far-travelled and world-famous old gentlemen Democritus, asking him questions on the atoms, on the shape of the earth, on moral conduct, God, and the immortality of the soul—without being denied on any of these points. Can you easily imagine such a motley conversation between a student and his teacher in our days? Yet, in all probability, quite a few young people have a similar—we should say quaint—collection of inquiries on their minds, and would like to discuss all of them with the one person of their confidence.

So much for the first of the two points that I announced my intention of submitting as clues to the renascent interest in ancient thought. Let me now put forward the second point, namely, the present crisis of the fundamental sciences.

Most of us believe that an ideally accomplished science of the happenings in space and time would be able to reduce them in principle to events that are completely accessible and understandable to (an ideally accomplished) physics. But it was from physics that, in the early years of the century, the first shocks—quantum theory and the theory of relativity—started to set the foundations of science trembling. During the great classical period of the nineteenth century, however remote might seem the realization of the task of actually describing in terms of physics the growth of a plant or the physiological processes in the brain of a human thinker or of a swallow building its nest, the language in which the account ought eventually to be drawn up was believed to be deciphered, namely: corpuscles, the ultimate constituents of matter, move under their mutual interaction, which is not instantaneous, but transmitted by a ubiquitous medium that one may or may not choose to call ether; the very terms 'movement' and 'transmission' imply that the measure and the scene of all this are time and space; these have no other property or task than to be the stage, as it were, on

which we image the corpuscles moving and their interaction being transmitted. Now, on the one hand, the rela-
tivistic theory of gravitation goes to show that the distinction between 'actor' and 'stage' is not expedient. Matter and the (field- or wave-like) propagation of something
transmitting the interaction ought better to be regarded as
the *shape* of space-time itself, which ought not to be
looked upon as being conceptually prior to what was
hitherto called its content; no more than, say, the corners
of a triangle are prior to the triangle. Quantum theory, on
the other hand, tells us that what was formerly considered
as the most obvious and fundamental property of the corpuscles, so much so that it was hardly even mentioned,
namely their being identifiable individuals, has only a
limited significance. Only when a corpuscle is moving
with sufficient speed in a region not too crowded with
corpuscles of the same kind does its identity remain
(nearly) unambiguous. Otherwise it becomes blurred.
And by this assertion we do not mean to indicate merely
our practical inability to follow the movement of the
particle in question; the very notion of absolute identity
is believed to be inadmissible. At the same time we are
told that the interaction, whenever it has—as it frequently
has—the form of waves of short wave-length and low
intensity, itself assumes the form of fairly well identifiable
particles—in the teeth of the aforesaid description as
waves. The particles which represent the interaction in
the course of its propagation are, in every particular case,
different in kind from those that interact; yet they have
the same claim to be called particles. To round off the
picture, particles of any kind exhibit the character of
waves, which becomes the more pronounced the slower
they move and the denser they crowd, with the corresponding loss of individuality.

The argument for whose sake I have inserted this brief
report would be reinforced by mentioning the 'pulling
down of the frontier between observer and observed'
which many consider an even more momentous revolution
of thought, while to my mind it seems a much overrated
provisional aspect without profound significance. Any-

how, my point is this. The modern development, which those who have brought it to the fore are yet far from really understanding, has intruded into the relatively simple scheme of physics which towards the end of the nineteenth century looked fairly stabilized. This intrusion has, in a way, overthrown what had been built on the foundations laid in the seventeenth century, mainly by Galileo, Huygens and Newton. The very foundations were shaken. Not that we are not everywhere still under the spell of this great period. We are all the time using its basic conceptions, though in a form their authors would hardly recognize. And at the same time we are aware that we are at the end of our tether. It is, then, natural to recall that the thinkers who started to mould modern science did not begin from schatch. Though they had little to borrow from the earlier centuries of our era, they very truly revived and continued ancient science and philosophy. From this source, awe-inspiring both by its remoteness in time and by its genuine grandeur, preconceived ideas and unwarranted assumptions may have been taken over by the fathers of modern science, and would, by their authority, soon be perpetuated. Had the highly flexible and open-minded spirit that pervaded antiquity continued, such points would have continued to be debated and could have been corrected. A prejudice is more easily detected in the primitive, ingenuous form in which it first arises than as the sophisticated, ossified dogma it is apt to become later. Science does appear to be baffled by ingrained habits of thought, some of which seem to be very difficult to find out, while others have already been discovered. The theory of relativity has done away with Newton's concepts of absolute space and time, in other words of absolute motionlessness and absolute simultaneity, and it has ousted the time-honoured couple 'force and matter' at least from its dominating position. Quantum theory, while extending atomism almost limitlessly, has at the same time plunged it into a crisis that is severer than most people are prepared to admit. On the whole the present crisis in modern basic science points to the necessity of revising its foundations down to very early layers.

This, then, is a further incentive for us to return once again to an assiduous study of Greek thought. There is not only, as was pointed out earlier in this chapter, the hope of unearthing obliterated wisdom, but also of discovering inveterate error at the source, where it is easier to recognize. By the serious attempt to put ourselves back into the intellectual situation of the ancient thinkers, far less experienced as regards the actual behaviour of nature, but also very often much less biased, we may regain from them their freedom of thought—albeit possibly in order to use it, aided by our superior knowledge of facts, for correcting early mistakes of theirs that may still be baffling us.

Let me conclude this chapter by some quotations. The first bears closely on what has just been said. It is translated from Theodor Gomperz's *Griechische Denker*.[4] To meet the possible objection that no practical advantage can spring from studying ancient opinion, which has been long superseded by better insight based on vastly superior information, a series of arguments is brought to the fore that ends with the following notable paragraph:

> It is of even greater importance to recall an *indirect* kind of application or utilization that . . . must be regarded as highly momentous. Nearly our entire intellectual education originates from the Greeks. A thorough knowledge of these origins is the indispensable prerequisite for *freeing* ourselves from their overwhelming influence. To ignore the past is here not merely undesirable, but simply impossible. You need not know of the doctrines and writings of the great masters of antiquity, of Plato and Aristotle, you need never have heard their names, none the less you are under the spell of their authority. Not only has their influence been passed on by those who took over from them in ancient and in modern times; our entire thinking, the logical categories in which it moves, the linguistic pat-

[4] Vol. i, p. 419 (3rd ed. 1911).

terns it uses (being therefore dominated by them)—all this is in no small degree an artifact and is, in the main, the product of the great thinkers of antiquity. We must, indeed, investigate this process of becoming in all thoroughness, lest we mistake for primitive what is the result of growth and development, and for natural what is actually artificial.

The following lines are taken from the Preface of John Burnet's *Early Greek Philosophy*: '. . . it is an adequate description of science to say that it is "thinking about the world in the Greek way". That is why science has never existed except among peoples who came under the influence of Greece.' This is the most concise justification a scientist could wish for, to excuse his propensity for 'wasting his time' in studies of this kind.

And an excuse seems to be needed. Ernst Mach, the physicist colleague of Gomperz at the University of Vienna, and eminent historian (!) of physics, had, a few decades earlier, spoken of the 'sparse and paltry remnants of ancient science'.[5] He continues thus:

> For our culture has gradually acquired full independence, soaring far above that of antiquity. It is following an entirely *new* trend. It centres around mathematical and scientific enlightenment. The traces of ancient ideas, still lingering in philosophy, jurisprudence, art and science, constitute impediments rather than assets, and will come to be untenable in the long run in face of the development of our own views.

For all its supercilious crudeness, Mach's view has a relevant point in common with what I have quoted from Gomperz, namely the plea for our having to *overcome* the Greeks. But while Gomperz supports a non-trivial turn by obviously true arguments, Mach clinches the trivial side by gross exaggeration. In other passages of the same paper he recommends a quaint method of getting beyond antiquity, namely to neglect and ignore it. In this, for all

[5] *Popular Lectures*, 3rd ed., essay no. xvii (J. A. Barth, 1903).

I know, he had little success—fortunately, for the mistakes of the great, promulgated along with the discoveries of their genius, are apt to work serious havoc.

## II. WHAT ARE THE SPECIAL FEATURES?*

Let me now, at last, approach the answer to the question which was put at the outset.

Remember the lines of Burnet's preface—that *science* is a Greek invention; that science has never existed except among peoples who came under Greek influnce. Later in the same book he says: 'The founder of the Milesian School and therefore [!] the first man of science was Thales.'[6] Gomperz says (I quoted him extensively) that our whole modern way of thinking is based on Greek thinking; it is therefore something special, something that has grown historically over many centuries, *not* the general, the only possible way of thinking about Nature. He sets much store on our becoming aware of this, of recognizing the peculiarities as such, possibly freeing us from their well-night irresistible spell.

What are they then? What are the peculiar, special traits of our scientific world-picture?

About one of these fundamental features there can be no doubt. It is the hypothesis that *the display of Nature can be understood.* I have touched on this point repeatedly. It is the non-spiritistic, the non-superstitious, the non-magical outlook. A lot more could be said about it. One would in this context have to discuss the questions: what does comprehensibility really mean, and in what sense, if any, does science give explanations? David Hume's (1711–76) great discovery that the relation between cause and effect is not directly observable and enunciates nothing but the regular succession—this fundamental epistemological discovery has led the great physi-

---

[6] *Early Greek Philosophy*, p. 40.

*Section II is the seventh and last Chapter of *Nature and the Greeks* (Cambridge, 1954), pp. 88–96.

cists, Gustav Kirchhoff (1824–87) and Ernst Mach (1838–1916), and others to maintain that natural science does not vouchsafe any explanations, that it aims only at, and is unable to attain to anything but, a complete and (Mach) economical description of the observed facts. This view, in the more elaborate form of philosophical positivism, has been enthusiastically embraced by modern physicists. It has great consistency; it is very difficult, if not impossible, to refute, rather like solipsism, but is very much more reasonable than the latter. Though the positivist view ostensibly contradicts the 'understandability of Nature', it is certainly not a return to the superstitious and magical outlook of yore; quite the contrary, from physics it expels the notion of force, the most dangerous relic of animism in this science. It is a salutary antidote against the rashness with which scientists are prone to believe that they have understood a phenomenon, when they have really only grasped the facts by describing them. Yet even from the positivists' point of view one ought not, so I believe, to declare that science conveys no understanding. For even if it be true (as they maintain) that in principle we only observe and register facts and put them into a convenient mnemotechnical arrangement, there are factual relations between our findings in the various, widely distant domains of knowledge, and again between them and the most fundamental general notions (as the natural integers 1, 2, 3, 4, . . .), relations so striking and interesting, that for our eventual grasping and registering them the term 'understanding' seems very appropriate. The most outstanding examples, to my mind, are the mechanical theory of heat, which amounts to a reduction to pure numbers; and similarly I would call Darwin's theory of evolution an instance of our gaining true insight. The same can be said about genetics, based on the discoveries of Mendel and de Vries, while in physics quantum theory has reached a promising outlook, but has not yet attained to full comprehensibility, though it is successful and helpful in many ways, even in genetics and biology in general.

There is, however, so I believe, a second feature, much

less clearly and openly displayed, but of equally fundamental importance. It is this, that science in its attempt
to describe and understand Nature simplifies this very
difficult problem. The scientist subconsciously, almost inadvertently, simplifies his problem of understanding Nature by disregarding or cutting out of the picture to be
constructed, himself, his own personality, the subject of
cognizance.

Inadvertently the thinker steps back into the role of
an external observer. This facilitates the task very much.
But it leaves gaps, enormous lacunae, leads to paradoxes
and antinomies whenever, unaware of this initial renunciation, one tries to find oneself in the picture or to put
oneself, one's own thinking and sensing mind, back into
the picture.

This momentous step—cutting out oneself, stepping
back into the position of an observer who has nothing to
do with the whole performance—has received other names,
making it appear quite harmless, natural, inevitable. It
might be called just objectivation, looking upon the world
as an object. The moment you do that, you have virtually
ruled yourself out. A frequently used expression is 'the
hypothesis of a real world around us' (*Hypothese der
realen Aussenwelt*). Why, only a fool would forgo it! Quite
right, only a fool. None the less it is a definite trait, a
definite feature of our way of understanding Nature—and
it has consequences.

The clearest vestiges of this idea that I have been able
to find in ancient Greek writing are certain fragments of
Heraclitus. For it is the *xunón* or *koinón,* the 'world in
common', of Heraclitus, that we are constructing; we are
hypostatizing the world as an object, making the assumption of a real world around us—as the most popular phrase
runs—made up of the overlapping parts of our several
consciousnesses. And in doing so, everyone willy-nilly
takes himself—the subject of cognizance, the thing that
says 'cogito ergo sum'—out of the world, removes himself
from it into the position of an external observer, who does
not himself belong to the party. The 'sum' becomes 'est'.

Is that really so, must it be so, and why is it so? For we

are not aware of it. I'll say presently why we are not aware of it. First let me say why it is so.

Well, the 'real world around us' and 'we ourselves', i.e. our minds, are made up of the same building material, the two consist of the same bricks, as it were, only arranged in a different order—sense perceptions, memory images, imagination, thought. It needs, of course, some reflexion, but one easily falls in with the fact that matter is composed of these elements and nothing else. Moreover, imagination and thought take an increasingly important part (as against crude sense-perception), as science, knowledge of nature, progresses.

What happens is this. We can think of these—let me call them *elements*—either as constituting mind, everyone's own mind, or as constituting the material world. But we cannot, or can only with great difficulty, think both things at the same time. To get from the mind-aspect to the matter-aspect or vice versa, we have, as it were, to take the elements asunder and to put them together again in an entirely different order. For example—it is not easy to give examples, but I'll try—my mind at this moment is constituted by all I sense around me: my own body, you all sitting in front of me and very kindly listening to me, the *aide-mémoire* in front of me, and, above all, the ideas I wish to explain to you, the suitable framing of them into words. But now envisage any one of the material objects around us, for example my arm and hand. As a material object it is composed, not only of my own direct sensations of it, but also of the imagined sensations I would have in turning it round, moving it, looking at it from all different angles; in addition it is composed of the perceptions I imagine you to have of it, and also, if you think of it purely scientifically, of all you could verify and would actually find if you took it and dissected it, to convince yourself of its intrinsic nature and composition. And so on. There is no end to enumerating all the potential percepts and sensations on my and on your side that are included in my speaking of this arm as of an objective feature of the 'real world around us'.

The following simile is not very good, but it is the best

I can think of: a child is given an elaborate box of bricks of various sizes and shapes and colours. It can build from them a house, or a tower, or a church, or the Chinese wall, etc. But it cannot build two of them at the same time, because it is, at least partly, the same bricks it needs in every case.

This is the reason why I believe it to be true that I actually do cut out of my mind when I construct the real world around me. And I am not aware of this cutting out. And then I am very astonished that the scientific picture of the real world around me is very deficient. It gives a lot of factual information, puts all our experience in a magnificently consistent order, but it is ghastly silent about all the sundry that is really near to our heart, that really matters to us. It cannot tell us a word about red and blue, bitter and sweet, physical pain and physical delight; it knows nothing of beautiful and ugly, good or bad, God and eternity. Science sometimes pretends to answer questions in these domains, but the answers are very often so silly that we are not inclined to take them seriously.

So in brief, we do not belong to this material world that science constructs for us. We are not in it, we are outside. We are only spectators. The reason why we believe that we are in it, that we belong to the picture, is that our bodies are in the picture. Our bodies belong to it. Not only my own body, but those of my friends, also of my dog and cat and horse, and of all the other people and animals. And this is my only means of communicating with them.

Moreover, my body is implied in quite a few of the more interesting changes—movements, etc.—that go on in this material world, and is implied in such a way that I feel myself partly the author of these goings-on. But then comes the impasse, this very embarrassing discovery of science, that I am not needed as an author. Within the scientific world-picture all these happenings take care of themselves, they are amply accounted for by direct energetic interplay. Even the human body's movements 'are its own' as Sherrington put it. The scientific world-picture vouchsafes a very complete understanding of all that happens—it makes it just a little too understandable. It allows you to imagine the total display as that of a mechanical clock-work, which for all that science knows could go on just the same as it does, without there being consciousness, will, endeavour, pain and delight and responsibility connected with it—though they actually are. And the reason for this disconcerting situation is just this, that, for the purpose of constructing the picture of the external world, we have used the greatly simplifying device of cutting our own personality out, removing it; hence it is gone, it has evaporated, it is ostensibly not needed.

In particular, and most importantly, this is the reason why the scientific world-view contains of itself no ethical values, no aesthetical values, not a word about our own ultimate scope or destination, and no God, if you please. Whence came I, whither go I?

Science cannot tell us a word about why music delights us, of why and how an old song can move us to tears.

Science, we believe, can, in principle, describe in full detail all that happens in the latter case in our sensorium and 'motorium' from the moment the waves of compression and dilation reach our ear to the moment when certain glands secrete a salty fluid that emerges from our eyes. But of the feelings of delight and sorrow that accompany the process science is completely ignorant—and therefore reticent.

Science is reticent too when it is a question of the great Unity—the One of Parmenides—of which we all somehow form part, to which we belong. The most popular name for it in our time is God—with a capital 'G'. Science is, very usually, branded as being atheistic. After what we said, this is not astonishing. If its world-picture does not even contain blue, yellow, bitter, sweet—beauty, delight and sorrow—, if personality is cut out of it by agreement, how should it contain the most sublime idea that presents itself to human mind?

The world is big and great and beautiful. My scientific knowledge of the events in it comprises hundreds of millions of years. Yet in another way it is ostensibly contained in a poor seventy or eighty or ninety years granted to me

—a tiny spot in immeasurable time, nay even in the finite millions and milliards of years that I have learnt to measure and to assess. Whence come I and whither go I? That is the great unfathomable question, the same for every one of us. Science has no answer to it. Yet science represents the level best we have been able to ascertain in the way of safe and incontrovertible knowledge.

However, our life as something like human beings has lasted, at the most, only about half a million years. From all that we know, we may anticipate, even on this particular globe, quite a few million years to come. And from all this we feel that any thought we attain to during this time will not have been thought in vain.

# Science and Humanism: The Spiritual Bearing of Science on Life*

What is the value of scientific research? Everybody knows that in our days more than ever before a man or a woman who wishes to make a genuine contribution to the advancement of science has to specialize: which means to intensify one's endeavour to learn all that is known within a certain narrow domain and then to try and increase this knowledge by one's own work—by studies, experiments, and thinking. Being engaged in such specialized activity one naturally at times stops to think what it is good for. Has the promotion of knowledge within a narrow domain any value in itself? Has the sum total of achievements in all the several branches of *one* science—say of physics, or chemistry, or botany, or zoology—any value in itself—or perhaps the sum total of the achievements of all the sciences together—and *what* value has it?

A great many people, particularly those not deeply interested in science, are inclined to answer this question by pointing to the practical consequences of scientific achievements in transforming technology, industry, engineering, etc., in fact in changing our whole way of life beyond recognition in the course of less than two centuries, with further and even more rapid changes to be expected in the time to come.

Few scientists will agree with this utilitarian appraisal of their endeavour. Questions of values are, of course, the most delicate ones; it is hardly possible to offer incontrovertible arguments. But let me give you the three principal ones by which I should try to oppose this opinion.

* From *Science and Humanism* (Cambridge: Cambridge University Press, 1951), 1–11.

Firstly, I consider natural science to be very much on the same line as the other kinds of learning—or *Wissenschaft*, to use the German expression—cultivated at our universities and other centres for the advancement of knowledge. Consider the study or research in history or languages, philosophy, geography—or history of music, painting, sculpture, architecture—or in archaeology and prehistory; nobody would like to associate with these activities, as their principal aim, the practical improvement of the conditions of human society, although improvement does result from them quite frequently. I cannot see that science has, in this respect, a different standing.

On the other hand (and this is my second argument), there are natural sciences which have obviously no practical bearing at all on the life of the human society: astrophysics, cosmology, and some branches of geophysics. Take, for instance, seismology. We know enough about earthquakes to know that there is very little chance of foretelling them, in the way of warning people to leave their houses, as we warn trawlers to return when a storm is drawing near. All that seismology could do is to warn prospective settlers of certain danger zones; but those, I am afraid, are mostly known by sad experience without the aid of science, yet they are often densely populated, the need for fertile soil being more pressing.

Thirdly, I consider it extremely doubtful whether the happiness of the human race has been enhanced by the technical and industrial developments that followed in the wake of rapidly progressing natural science. I cannot here enter into details, and I will not speak of the future development—the surface of the earth getting infected with artificial radio-activity, with the gruesome consequences for our race, depicted by Aldous Huxley in his interesting recent novel (*Ape and Essence*). But consider only the 'marvellous reduction of size' of the world by the fantastic modern means of traffic. All distances have been reduced to almost nothing, when measured not in miles but in hours of *quickest* transport. But when measured in the costs of even the *cheapest* transport they have been doubled or trebled even in the last ten or twenty years. The result is that many families and groups of close friends have been scattered over the globe as never before. In many cases they are not rich enough ever to meet again, in others they do so under terrible sacrifices for a short time ending in a heart-rending farewell. Does this make for human happiness? These are a few striking examples; one could enlarge on the topic for hours.

But let us turn to less gloomy aspects of human activities. You may ask—you are bound to ask me now: What, then, is in your opinion the value of natural science? I answer: Its scope, aim and value is the same as that of any other branch of human knowledge. Nay, none of them alone, only the union of all of them, has any scope or value at all, and that is simply enough described: it is to obey the command of the Delphic deity, *Gnôthi seautón*, get to know yourself. Or, to put it in the brief, impressive rhetoric of Plotinus (*Enn.* VI, 4, 14): *hēmeîs dè, tínes dè hēmeîs;* 'And we, who are we anyhow?' He continues: 'Perhaps we were *there* already before this creation came into existence, human beings of another type, or even some sort of gods, pure souls and mind united with the whole universe, parts of the intelligible world, not separated and cut off, but at one with the whole.'

I am born into an environment—I know not whence I came nor whither I go nor who I am. This is my situation as yours, every single one of you. The fact that everyone always was in this same situation, and always will be, tells me nothing. Our burning question as to the whence and whither—all we can ourselves observe about it is the present environment. That is why we are eager to find out about it as much as we can. That is science, learning, knowledge, that is the true source of every spiritual endeavour of man. We try to find out as much as we can about the spatial and temporal surrounding of the place in which we find ourselves put by birth. And as we try, we delight in it, we find it extremely interesting. (May *that* not be the end for which we are there?)

It seems plain and self-evident, yet it needs to be said: the isolated knowledge obtained by a group of specialists in a narrow field has in itself no value whatsoever, but only in its synthesis with all the rest of knowledge and only inasmuch as it really contributes in this synthesis something toward answering the demand *tínes dè hēmeîs* ['who are we']?

José Ortega y Gasset, the great Spanish philosopher, who is now after many years of exile back in Madrid (though he is, I believe, just as little a fascist as a *sozial-demokrat*, but just an ordinary reasonable person), published in the twenties of this century a series of articles, which were later collected in a delightful volume under the title of *La rebelión de las masas*—the rebellion of the masses. It has, by the way, nothing to do with social or other revolutions, the *rebelión* is meant purely metaphorically. The Age of Machinery has resulted in sending the numbers of the populations and the volume of their needs up to enormous heights, unprecedented and unforeseeable. The daily life of every one of us becomes more and more entangled with the necessity of coping with these numbers. Whatever we need or desire, a loaf of bread or a pound of butter, a bus-lift or a theatre-ticket, a quiet holiday resort or the permit to travel abroad, a room to live in or a job to live on . . . there are always many, many others having the same need or desire. The new situations and developments that have turned up as the result of this unparalleled soaring of the numbers form the subject of Ortega's book.

It contains extremely interesting observations. Just to give you an example—though it does not concern us at the moment—one chapter-heading reads *El mayor peligro, el estado*: the greatest danger—the state. He there declares the increasing power of the state in curtailing individual freedom—under the pretext of protecting us, but far beyond necessity—to be the greatest danger to the future development of culture (*kultur*). But the chapter I wish to speak of here is the preceding one; it is entitled *La barbarie del 'especialismo'*: the barbarism of specialization. At first sight it seems paradoxical and it may shock you. He makes bold to picture the specialized scientist as the typical representative of the brute ignorant rabble—the *hombre masa* (mass-man)—who endanger the survival of true civilization. I can only pick out a few passages from the delightful description he gives of this 'type of scientist without precedent in history'.

> He is a person who, of all the things that a truly educated person ought to know of, is familiar only with one particular science, nay even of this science only that small portion is known to him in which he himself is engaged in research. He reaches the point where he proclaims it a virtue not to take any notice of all that remains outside the narrow domain he himself cultivates, and denounces as *dilettantist* the curiosity that aims at the synthesis of all knowledge.

> It comes to pass that he, secluded in the narrowness of his field of vision, actually succeeds in discovering new facts and in promoting his science (which he hardly knows) and promoting along with it the integrated human thought—which he with full determination ignores. How has anything like this been possible, and how does it continue to be possible? For we must strongly underline the inordinateness of this undeniable fact: experimental science has been advanced to a considerable extent by the work of fabulously mediocre and even less than mediocre persons.

I shall not continue the quotation, but I strongly recommend you to get hold of the book and continue for yourself. In the twenty-odd years that have passed since the first publication, I have noticed very promising traces of opposition to the deplorable state of affairs denounced by Ortega. Not that we can avoid specialization altogether; that is impossible if we want to get on. Yet the awareness that specialization is not a virtue but an unavoidable evil is gaining ground, the awareness that all specialized research has real value only in the context of the integrated totality of knowledge. The voices become fainter and fainter that accuse a man of dilettantism who dares to think and speak and write on topics that require more than the special training for which he is 'licensed' or 'qualified'. And any loud barking at such attempts comes from very special quarters of two types—either very scientific or very unscientific quarters—and the reasons for the barking are in both cases translucent.

In an article on 'The German Universities' (published on 11 December 1949 in *The Observer*) Robert Birley, Headmaster of Eton, quoted some lines from the report of the Commission for University Reform in Germany—quoted them very emphatically, an emphasis that I fully endorse. The following is said in this report:

> Each lecturer in a technical university should possess the following abilities:
> (a) To see the limits of his subject matter. In his teaching to make the students aware of these limits, and to show them that beyond these limits forces come into play which are no longer entirely rational, but arise out of life and human society itself.
> (b) To show in every subject the way that leads beyond its own narrow confines to broader horizons of its own. Etc.

I won't say that these formulations are peculiarly original, but who would expect originality of a committee or commission or board or that sort of thing?—mankind *en masse* is always very commonplace. Yet one is glad and thankful to find this sort of attitude prevailing. The only criticism—if it be a criticism—is that one can see no earthly reason why these demands should be restricted to the teachers at *technical* universities in *Germany*. I believe they apply to *any* teacher at *any* university, nay, at any school in the world; I should formulate the demand thus:

Never lose sight of the role your particular subject has within the great performance of the tragi-comedy of human life; keep in touch with life—not so much with practical life as with the ideal background of life, which is ever so much more important; and, *Keep life in touch with you.* If you cannot—in the long run—tell everyone what you have been doing, your doing has been worthless.

I regard the public lectures which the statute of the Institute prescribes for us to deliver every year as one of the means for establishing and keeping up this contact in our small domain. Indeed I consider this to be their exclusive scope. The task is not very easy. For one has to have some kind of background to start from, and, as you know, scientific education is fabulously neglected, not only in this or that country—though, indeed, in some more than in others. This is an evil that is inherited, passed on from generation to generation. The majority of educated persons are not interested in science, and are not aware that scientific knowledge forms part of the idealistic background of human life. Many believe—in their complete ignorance of what science really is—that it has mainly the ancillary task of inventing new machinery, or helping to invent it, for improving our conditions of life. They are prepared to leave this task to the specialists, as they leave the repairing of their pipes to the plumber. If persons with this outlook decide upon the curriculum of our children, the result is necessarily such as I have just described it.

There are, of course, historical reasons why this attitude still prevails. The bearing of science on the idealistic background of life has always been great—apart perhaps from the Dark Ages, when science practically did not exist in Europe. But it must be confessed that there has been a lull also in more recent times, which could easily deceive one into underrating the idealistic task of science. I place the lull about in the second half of the nineteenth century. This was a period of enormous explosion-like development of science, and along with it of a fabulous, explosion-like development of industry and engineering which had such a tremendous influence on the material features of human life that most people forgot any other connexions. Nay, worse than that! The fabulous *material* development led to a *materialistic* outlook, allegedly derived from the new scientific discoveries. These occurrences have, I think, contributed to the deliberate neglect of science in many quarters during the half century that followed—the one that is just drawing to a close. For there always is a certain time-lag between the views held by learned men and the views held by the general public about the views of those learned men. I do not think that fifty years is an excessive estimate for the average length of that time-lag.

Be that as it may, the fifty years that have just gone by —the first half of the twentieth century—have seen a development of science in general, and of physics in particular, unsurpassed in transforming our Western outlook on what has often been called the Human Situation. I have little doubt that it will take another fifty years or so before the educated section of the general public will have become aware of this change. Of course, I am not so much of an idealistic dreamer as to hope substantially to accelerate this process by a couple of public lectures. But, on the other hand, this process of *assimilation* is not automatic. *We have to labour for it.* In this labour I take my share, trusting that others will take theirs. It is part of our task in life.

# The Future of Understanding

We may, I believe, regard it as extremely improbable that our understanding of the world represents any definite or final stage, a maximum or optimum in any respect. By this I do *not* mean merely that the continuation of our research in the various sciences, our philosophical studies and religious endeavour, is likely to enhance and improve our present outlook. What we are likely to gain in this way in the next, say, two and a half millennia—estimating it by what we have gained since Protagoras, Democritus and Antisthenes—is insignificant compared with what I am here alluding to. There is no reason whatever for believing that our brain is the supreme *ne plus ultra* of an organ of thought in which God's world is reflected. It is more likely than not that a species could acquire a similar contraption whose corresponding imagery compared with ours as ours with that of the dog, or his in turn with that of a snail.

If this be so, then—though it is not relevant in principle —it interests us, as it were for personal reasons, whether anything of the sort could be reached on our globe by our own offspring or the offspring of some of us. The globe is all right. It is a fine young leasehold, to run under acceptable conditions of living still for at least the time it took us (about 1000 million years) to develop into what we are from the earliest beginnings. But are *we* all right? If one accepts the present theory of evolution—and we have no better—it might seem that we have been very nearly cut off from future evolution. Is there still physical evolution to be expected in man, I mean to say relevant changes in our physique that become gradually fixed as inherited features, just as our present bodily self is fixed by inheritance—genotypical changes, to use the technical term of the biologist? This question is difficult to answer. We may be approaching the bottom of a blind alley, we may even have reached it. This would not be an exceptional event and it would not mean that our species would have to become extinct very soon. From the geological records we know that some species or even large groups seem to have reached the end of their evolutionary possibilities a very long time ago, yet they have not died out, but remained unchanged, or without appreciable change, for many millions of years. The tortoises, for instance, and the crocodiles are in this sense very old groups, relics of a far remote past; we are also told that the whole large group of *insects* are more or less in the same boat—and they comprise a greater number of separate species than all the rest of the animal kingdom taken together. But they have changed very little in millions of years, while the rest of the living surface of the earth has during this time undergone change beyond recognition. What barred further evolution in the insects was probably this, that they had adopted the plan—you will not misunderstand this figurative expression—that they had adopted the plan of wearing their skeleton outside instead of inside, as we do. Such an outside armour, while affording protection in addition to mechanical stability, *cannot grow* as the bones of a mammal do between birth and maturity. This circumstance is bound to render gradual adaptive changes in the life history of the individual very difficult.

In the case of man several arguments seem to militate against further evolution. The spontaneous inheritable changes (now called *mutations*) from which, according to Darwin's theory, the 'profitable' ones are automatically selected, are as a rule only small evolutionary steps, affording, if any, only a slight advantage. That is why in Darwin's deductions an important part is attributed to the usually enormous abundance of offspring, of which only a very small fraction can possibly survive. For only thus

does a small amelioration in the chance of survival seem
to have a reasonable likelihood of being realized. This
whole mechanism appears to be blocked in civilized man—
in some respects even reversed. We are, generally speaking, not willing to see our fellow-creatures suffer and
perish, and so we have gradually introduced legal and
social institutions which on the one hand protect life,
condemn systematic infanticide, try to help every sick or
frail human being to survive, while on the other hand
they *have to* replace the natural elimination of the less
fit by keeping the offspring within the limits of the available livelihood. This is achieved partly in a direct way, by
birth control, partly by preventing a considerable pro-
portion of females from mating. Occasionally—as this
generation knows all too well—the insanity of war and all
the disaster and blunder that follow in its wake contribute
their share to the balance. Millions of adults and children
of both sexes are killed by starvation, exposure, epidemics.
While in the far remote past the warfare between small
tribes or clans is supposed to have had a positive selectional value, it seems doubtful whether it ever had in
historical times, and doubtless that war at present has
none. It means an indiscriminate killing, just as the ad-
vances in medicine and surgery result in an indiscriminate
saving of lives. While justly and diametrically opposite in
our esteem yet both, war and medical art, seem to be of
no selectional value whatever.

These considerations suggest that as a developing
species we have come to a standstill and have little prospect of further biological advance. Even if this were so,
it need not bother us. We might survive without any
biological change for millions of years, like the crocodiles
and many insects. Still, from a certain philosophical point
of view the idea is depressing, and I should like to try and
make out a case for the contrary. To do so I must enter
on a certain aspect of the theory of evolution which I
find supported in Professor Julian Huxley's well-known
book *Evolution: The Modern Synthesis*, an aspect which,

according to him, is not always sufficiently appreciated by recent evolutionists.

Popular expositions of Darwin's theory are apt to lead you to a gloomy and discouraging view, on account of the apparent passivity of the organism in the process of evolution. Mutations occur spontaneously in the gene—the 'hereditary substance'. We have reason to believe that they are mainly due to what the physicist calls a thermodynamic fluctuation—in other words to pure chance. The individual has not the slightest influence on the hereditary treasure it receives from its parents, nor on the one it leaves to its offspring. Mutations that occur are acted on by 'natural selection of the fittest'. This again seems to mean pure chance, since it means that a favourable mutation increases the prospect for the individual of survival and of begetting offspring, to which it transmits the mutation in question. Apart from this, its activity during its lifetime seems to be biologically irrelevant. For, nothing of it has any influence on the offspring. *Acquired properties are not inherited.* Any skill or training attained is lost, it leaves no trace, it dies with the individual, it is not transmitted. An intelligent being in this situation would find that nature, as it were, refuses his collaboration—she does all herself, dooms the individual to inactivity, indeed to nihilism.

As you know, Darwin's theory was not the first systematic theory of evolution. It was preceded by the theory of Lamarck, which rests entirely on the assumption that any new features an individual has acquired by specific surroundings or behaviour during its lifetime before procreation can be, and usually are, passed on to its progeny, if not entirely, at least in traces. Thus if an animal by living on rocky or sandy soil produced protecting calluses on the soles of its feet, this callosity would gradually become hereditary so that later generations would receive it as a free gift without the hardship of acquiring it. In the same way the strength or skill or even substantial adaptation produced in any organ by its being continually used for certain ends, would not be lost, but passed on, at least partly, to the offspring. This view does not only afford a very simple understanding of the amazingly elaborate and specific adaptation to environment which is so characteristic of all living creatures. It is also beautiful, elating, encouraging and invigorating. It is infinitely more attractive than the gloomy aspect of passivity apparently offered by Darwinism. An intelligent being which considers itself a link in the long chain of evolution may, under Lamarck's theory, be confident that its striving efforts to improve its abilities, both bodily and mental, are not lost in the biological sense but form a small but integrating part of the striving of the species towards higher and ever higher perfection.

Unhappily Lamarckism is untenable. The fundamental assumption on which it rests, viz. that acquired properties can be inherited, is wrong. To the best of our knowledge they are not. The single steps of evolution are those spontaneous and fortuitous mutations which have nothing to do with the behaviour of the individual during its lifetime. And so we appear to be thrown back on the gloomy aspect of Darwinism that I have depicted above.

I now wish to show you that this is not quite so. Without changing anything in the basic assumptions of Darwinism, we can see that the behaviour of the individual, the way it makes use of its innate faculties, plays a relevant part, nay, plays the most relevant part, in evolution. There is a very true kernel in Lamarck's view, namely that there is an irrescindable causal connexion between the functioning, the actually being put to profitable use, of a character—an organ, any property or ability or bodily feature—and its being developed in the course of generations, and gradually improved for the purposes for which it is profitably used. This connexion, I say, between being used and being improved was a very correct cognition of Lamarck's, and it subsists in our present Darwinistic outlook, but it is easily overlooked on viewing Darwinism superficially. The course of events is almost the same *as if* Lamarckism were right, only the 'mechanism' by which things happen is more complicated than Lamarck thought. The point is not quite easy to explain or to grasp, and so it may be useful to summarize the result in advance. To avoid vagueness, let us thing of an *organ,* though the feature in question might be any property, habit, device, behaviour, or even any small addition to, or modification of, such a feature. Lamarck thought that the organ (a) is used, (b) is thus improved and (c) the improvement is transmitted to the offspring. This is wrong. We have to think that the organ (a) undergoes chance variations, (b) *the profitably used ones* are accumulated or at least accentuated by selection, (c) this continues from generation to generation, the selected mutations constituting a lasting improvement. The most striking *simulation* of Lamarckism occurs—according to Julian Huxley—when the initial variations that inaugurate the process are not true mutations, not yet of the inheritable type. Yet, if profitable, they may be accentuated by what he calls *organic selection,* and, so to speak, pave the way for true mutations to be immediately seized upon when they happen to turn up in the 'desirable' direction.

Let us now go into some details. The most important point is to see that a new character or modification of a character, acquired by variation, by mutation, or by mutation plus some little selection, may easily arouse the organism in relation to its environment to an activity that tends to increase the usefulness of that chcaracter and hence the 'grip' of selection on it. By possessing the new or changed character the individual may be caused to *change* its environment—either by actually *transforming* it, or by *migration*—or it may be caused to change its behaviour towards its environment, all this in a fashion so as strongly to reinforce the usefulness of the new character and thus to speed up its further selective improvement in the same direction.

This assertion may strike you as daring, since it seems to require purpose on the side of the individual, and even a high degree of intelligence. But I wish to make the point that my statement, while it includes, of course, the intelligent, purposeful behaviour of the higher animals, is by no means restricted to them. Let us give a few simple examples:

Not all the individuals of a population have exactly the same environment. Some of the flowers of a wild species happen to grow in the shadow, some in sunny spots, some in the higher ranges of a lofty mountain-slope, some in the lower parts or in the valley. A mutation—say hairy foliage—which is beneficial at higher altitude, will be favoured by selection in the higher ranges but will be 'lost' in the valley. The effect is the same as if the hairy mutants had migrated towards an environment that will favour further mutations that occur in the same direction.

Another example: Their ability to fly enables birds to build their nests high up in the trees where their young ones are less accessible to some of their enemies. Primarily those who took to it had a selectional advantage. The second step is that this kind of abode was bound to select the proficient fliers among the young ones. Thus a certain ability to fly produces a change of environment, or behaviour towards the environment, which favours an accumulation of the same ability.

The most remarkable feature among living beings is that they are divided into species which are, many of them, so incredibly specialized on quite particular, often tricky performances, on which they rely especially for survival. A zoological garden is almost a curiosity show, and would be much more so could it include an insight into the life history of insects. Non-specialization is the exception. The rule is specialization in peculiar studied tricks which 'nobody would think of if nature had not made them'. It is difficult to believe that they all have resulted from Darwinian 'accumulation by chance'. Whether one wants it or not, one is taken by the impression of forces or tendencies away from 'the plain and simple' in certain directions towards the complicated. The 'plain and simple' seems to represent an unstable state of affairs. A departure from it provokes forces—so it seems—towards a further departure *in the same direction*. That would be difficult to understand if the development of a particular device, mechanism, organ, useful behaviour, were produced by a long pearl-string of chance events, independent of each other, as one is used to think in terms of Darwin's original conception. Actually, I believe, only the first small start 'in a certain direction' has this structure. It itself produces circumstances which 'hammer the plastic material'—by selection—more and more systematically in the direction of the advantage gained at the outset. In metaphorical speech one might say: the species has found out in which direction its chance in life lies, and pursues this path.

We must try to understand in a general way and to formulate in a non-animistic fashion how a chance mutation, which gives the individual a certain advantage and favours its survival in a given environment, should tend to do more than that, namely to increase the opportunities for its being profitably made use of, so as to concentrate on itself, as it were, the selective influence of the environment.

To reveal this mechanism let the environment be schematically described as an ensemble of favourable and unfavourable circumstances. Among the first are food, drink, shelter, sunlight and many others, among the latter are the dangers from other living beings (enemies), poisons and the roughness of the elements. For brevity we shall refer to the first kind as 'needs' and to the second as 'foes'. Not every need can be obtained, not every foe avoided. But a *living* species must have acquired a behaviour *that strikes a compromise* in avoiding the deadliest foes and satisfying the most urgent needs from the sources of easiest access, so that it *does* survive. A favourable mutation makes certain sources more easily accessible or reduces the danger from certain foes or both. It thereby increases the chance of survival of the individuals endowed with it, but in addition *it shifts the most favourable compromise,* because it changes the relative *weights* of those needs or foes on which it bears. Individuals which, by chance or intelligence, change their behaviour will accordingly be more favoured, and thus selected. This

change of behaviour is not transmitted to the next generation *by the gene*, not by direct inheritance, but this does
not mean that it is not transmitted. The simplest, most
primitive example is afforded by our species of flowers
(with a habitat along an extended mountain slope) that
develops a hairy mutant. The hairy mutants, favoured
mainly in the top ranges, disperse their seeds in the top
ranges, so that the next generation of 'hairies' taken as a
whole has 'climbed up the slope', as it were, 'to make
better use of their favourable mutation'.

In all this one must bear in mind that as a rule the
whole situation is extremely dynamic, the struggle is a
very stiff one. In a fairly prolific population that, at the
time, survives without appreciably increasing, the 'foes'
*usually* overpower the 'needs'—individual survival is an
exception. Moreover foes and needs are frequently
coupled, so that a pressing need can only be met by
braving a certain foe. (For instance, the antelope has to
come to the river for drink, but the lion knows the place
just as well as he.) The total pattern of foes and needs is
intricately interwoven. Thus a slight reduction of a certain
danger by a given mutation may make a considerable
difference for *those* mutants who brave that danger and
thereby avoid others. This may result in a noticeable selection not only of the genetic feature in question but also
with regard to the (intended or haphazard) skill in using
it. That kind of behaviour is transmitted to the offspring
by example—by *learning*, in a generalized sense of the
word. The shift of behaviour, in turn, enhances the selective value of any further mutation in the same direction.

The effect of such a display may have great similarity
to the mechanism as pictured by Lamarck. Though neither
an acquired behaviour nor any physical change that it
entails is directly transmitted to the offspring, yet behaviour has an important say in the process. But the causal
connexion is not what Lamarck thought it to be, rather
just the other way round. Not the behaviour changes the
physique of the parents and, by physical inheritance, that
of the offspring. It is the physical change in the parents
that modifies—directly or indirectly, by selection—their

behaviour; and this change of behaviour is, by example or teaching or even more primitively, transmitted to the progeny, along with the physical change carried by the gene. Nay, even if the physical change is not yet an inheritable one, the transmission of the induced behaviour "by teaching" can be a highly efficient evolutionary factor, because it throws the door open to receive future *inheritable* mutations with a prepared readiness to make the best use of them and thus to subject them to intense selection.

One might object that what we have here described may happen occasionally, but cannot continue indefinitely to form the essential mechanism of adaptive evolution. For, the change of behaviour is not itself transmitted by physical inheritance, by the hereditary substance, the choromosomes. It is therefore at first certainly not fixed genetically and it is difficult to see how it should ever come to be incorporated in the hereditary treasure. This is an important problem in itself. For we do know that habits are inherited, as, for instance, habits of nest-building in the birds, the various habits of cleanliness we observe in our dogs and cats, to mention a few obvious examples. If this could not be understood along orthodox Darwinian lines, Darwinism would have to be abandoned. The question becomes a singular significance in its application to man, since we wish to infer that the striving and labouring of a man during his lifetime constitute an integrating contribution to the development of the species, in the quite strict biological sense as well. I believe the situation to be, briefly, as follows.

According to our assumptions the behaviour changes parallel to the physique, first as a consequence of a chance change of the latter, but very soon directing the further selectional mechanism into definite channels, because, according as behaviour has availed itself of the first rudimentary benefits, only further mutations in the same direction have any selective value. But as—let me say— the new organ develops, behaviour becomes more and more bound up with its mere possession. Behaviour and physique mix into one. You simply cannot possess clever hands without using them for obtaining your aims, they would be in your way (as they often are to an amateur on the stage, because he has only fictitious aims). You cannot have efficient wings without attempting to fly. You cannot have a modulated organ of speech without trying to imitate the noises you hear around you. To distinguish between the possession of an organ and the urge to use it and to increase its skill by practice, to regard them as two different characteristics of the organism in question, would be an artificial distinction, made possible by an abstract language but having no counterpart in nature. We must, of course, not think that 'behaviour' after all gradually intrudes into the chromosome structure (or what not) and acquires 'loci' there. It is the new organs themselves (and they do become genetically fixed) that carry along with them the habit and the way of using them. Selection would be powerless in 'producing' a new organ, if selection were not aided all along by the organism's making appropriate use of it. And this is very essential. For in this way the two things go quite parallel and are ultimately, or indeed at every stage, fixed genetically as one thing: *a used organ*—as if Lamarck were right.

It is illuminating to compare this natural process with the making of an instrument by man. At first sight there appears to be a marked contrast. If *we* manufacture a delicate mechanism, we should in most cases spoil it, if we were impatient and tried to use it again and again long before it was finished. Nature, one is inclined to say, proceeds differently. She cannot produce a new organism and its organs otherwise than whilst they are continually used, probed, examined, with regard to their efficiency. *But actually this parallel is wrong.* The making of a single instrument by man corresponds to ontogenesis, that is, to the growing up of a single individual from the seed to maturity. Here too interference is not welcome. The young ones must be protected, they must not be put to work before they have acquired the full strength and skill of their species. The true parallel of the evolutionary development of organisms could be illustrated, e.g., by a historical exhibition of bicycles, showing how this machine gradually changed from year to year, from decade to decade; or in the same way of railway engines, motorcars, aeroplanes, typewriters, etc. Here, just as in the natural process, it is obviously essential that the machine in question should be continually used *and thus improved;* not literally improved by use, but by the experience gained and the alterations suggested. The bicycle, by the way, illustrates the case, mentioned before, of an *old* organism, which has reached the attainable perfection and has therefore pretty well ceased to undergo further changes. Still it is not about to become extinct!

Let us now return to the beginning of these talks. We started from the question: Is further biological development in man likely? Our discussion has, I believe, brought to the fore two relevant points.

The first is the biological importance of behaviour. By conforming to innate faculties as well as to the environment, and by adapting itself to changes in either of these factors, behaviour, though not itself inherited, may yet speed up the process of evolution by orders of magnitude. While in plants and in the lower ranges of the animal kingdom adequate behaviour is brought about by the slow process of selection, in other words by trial and error, man's high intelligence enables him to enact it by choice. This incalculable advantage may easily outweigh his handicap of slow and comparatively scarce propagation, which is further reduced by the biologically dangerous consideration not to let our offspring exceed the volume for which livelihood can be secured.

The second point (concerning the question whether biological development is still to be expected in man) is intimately connected with the first. In a way we get the full answer, viz. *This will depend on us and our doing.* We must not wait for things to come, believing that they are decided by irrescindable destiny. If we want it, we must do something about it. If not, not. Just as the political and social development and the sequence of historical events in general are not thrust upon us by the spinning of the Fates, but largely depend on our own doing, so our biological future, being nothing else but history on the large scale, must not be taken to be an unalterable destiny that is decided in advance by any law of Nature. To us at any rate, who are the acting subjects in the play, it is not, even though to a superior being, watching us as we watch the birds and the ants, it might appear to be. The reason why man tends to regard history, in the narrower and in the wider sense, as a predestined happening, controlled by rules and laws that he cannot change, is very obvious. It is because every single individual feels that he by himself has very little say in the matter, unless he can put his opinions over to many others and persuade them to regulate their behaviour accordingly.

As regards the concrete behaviour, necessary to secure our biological future, I will only mention one general point that I consider of primary importance. We are, I believe, at the moment in grave danger of missing the 'path to perfection'. From all that has been said, *selection* is an indispensable requisite for biological development. If it is entirely ruled out, development stops, nay, it may be reversed. To put it in the words of Julian Huxley:

'. . . the preponderance of degenerative (loss) mutation will result in degeneration of an organ when it becomes useless and selection is accordingly no longer acting on it to keep it up to the mark'. Now, I believe that the increasing mechanization and 'stupidization' of most manufacturing processes involve the serious danger of a general degeneration of our organ of intelligence. The more the chances in life of the clever and of the unresponsive worker are equalled out by the repression of handicraft and the spreading of tedious and boring work on the assembly line, the more will a good brain, clever hands and a sharp eye become superfluous. Indeed the unintelligent man, who naturally finds it easier to submit to the boring toil, will be favoured: he is likely to find it easier to thrive, to settle down and to beget offspring. The result may easily amount even to a negative selection as regards talents and gifts.

The hardship of modern industrial life has led to certain

institutions calculated to mitigate it, such as protection of the workers against exploitation and unemployment, and many other welfare and security measures. They are duly regarded as beneficial and they have become indispensable. Still, we cannot shut our eyes to the fact that, by alleviating the responsibility of the individual to look after himself and by levelling the chances of every man, they also tend to rule out the competition of talents and thus to put an efficient brake on biological evolution. I realize that this particular point is highly controversial. One may make a strong case, that the care for our present welfare must override the worry about our evolutionary future. But fortunately, so I believe, they go together, according to my main argument. Next to want, boredom has become the worst scourge in our lives. Instead of letting the ingenious machinery we have invented produce an increasing amount of superfluous luxury, we must planfully develop it so that it takes off human beings all the unintelligent, mechanical, 'machine-like' handling. The machine must take over the toil for which man is too good, not man the work for which the machine is too expensive, as quite often happens. This will not tend to make production cheaper, but those who are engaged in it happier. There is small hope of putting this through as long as the competition between big firms and concerns all over the world prevails. But this kind of competition is as uninteresting as it is biologically worthless. Our aim should be to reinstate in its place the interesting and intelligent competition of the single human beings.

# Are There Quantum Jumps?

'. . . cominciai a credere, che uno, che lascia un'opinione imbevuta col latte, e seguita da infiniti, per venire in un' altra da pochissimi seguita, e negata da tuttle le scuole, e che veramente sembra un paradosso grandissimo, bisognasse per necessità, che fusse mosso, per non dir forzato, da ragioni più efficaci.'[1]

GALILEO, Dialogue on the Two Greatest World Systems, 2nd Day.

## 1. The Cultural Background

Physical science, which aims not only at devising fascinating new experiments, but at obtaining a rational understanding of the results of observations, incurs at present, so I believe, the grave danger of getting severed from its historical background. The innovations of thought in the last fifty years, great and momentous and unavoidable as they were, are usually overrated compared with those of the preceding century; and the disproportionate foreshortening, by time-perspective, of previous achievements on which all our enlightenment in modern times depends, reaches a disconcerting degree according as earlier and earlier centuries are considered. Along with this disregard for historical linkage there is a tendency to forget that all

[1] . . . I began to believe that a man who gives up an opinion that he drank in with his mother's milk, and that is accepted by people without number, to arrive at another that is accepted by very few, and denied by all the schools, and that really seems a very great paradox, must needs have been moved, not to say forced, to do so, by more powerful reasons.

science is bound up with human culture in general, and that scientific findings, even those which at the moment appear the most advanced and esoteric and difficult to grasp, are meaningless outside their cultural context. A theoretical science, unaware that those of its constructs considered relevant and momentous are destined eventually to be framed in concepts and words that have a grip on the educated community and become part and parcel of the general world-picture—a theoretical science, I say, where this is forgotten, and where the initiated continue musing to each other in terms that are, at best, understood by a small group of close fellow-travellers, will necessarily be cut off from the rest of cultural mankind; in the long run it is bound to atrophy and ossify, however virulently esoteric chat may continue within its joyfully isolated groups of experts. This has happened before in similar circumstances. Benjamin Farrington puts it admirably in his *Greek Science,*[2] vol. 2, p. 173:

> Perhaps the most decisive defeat of the scientific spirit in antiquity had been the loss of the sense of history. History is the most fundamental science, for there is no human knowledge which cannot lose its scientific character when men forget the conditions under which it originated, the questions which it answered, and the functions it was created to serve. A great part of the mysticism and superstition of educated men consists of knowledge which has broken loose from its historical moorings.

The disregard for historical connectedness, nay, the pride of embarking on new ways of thought, of production and of action, the keen endeavour of shaking off, as it were, the indebtedness to our predecessors, are no doubt a general trend of our time. In the fine arts we notice strong currents quite obviously informed by this vein; we witness its results in modern painting, sculpture, architecture, music and poetry. There are many who look upon this as a new buoyant rise, while others regard it as a flaring up that inaugurates decay. This is not the place to

[2] Pelican Books, London, 1949.

dwell on this question, and my personal views on it might interest nobody. But I may say that whenever this trend enters science, it ought to be opposed. There obviously is a certain danger of its intruding into science in general, which is not an isolated enterprise of the human spirit, but grows on the same historic soil as the others and participates in the mood of the age. There is, however, so I believe, no other nearly so blatant example of this happening as the theories of physical science in our time. I believe that we are here facing a development which is the precise counterpart of that in the fine arts alluded to above. The most appropriate expression to use for it is one borrowed from the history of poetry: Góngorism. It refers to the poetry of the Spaniard Luis de Góngora (1561–1627), very fine poems, by the way, especially the early ones. Yet his later poems (to which the term more particularly refers) also sound good, and *they all make sense*. But he uses all his acuity and skill on making it as difficult as possible for the reader to unravel the sense, so that even natives of Castile use extended commentaries to grasp the meaning safely.

One ought not, I think, to say that if, in this, physics is following a general trend of our time, we must not oppose it. Though we are entirely the product of historical development, yet it is we who make its continuation and not history that drags us along a predestined trail. It depends entirely on us, on our stopping to think and acting according to reason, whether there will be decay or a new rise after the crisis. This is what Bertrand Russell in recent years has not tired of inculcating with regard to much more momentous questions than the fate of theoretical physics. However, here we shall be concerned with the latter.

My friend and scientific colleague Professor Hans Thirring, in his book *Homo Sapiens*,[3] in which he conducts an elaborate and very creditable campaign against War, and for Universal Peace, incidentally opines that in antiquity everybody except a few men of genius considered the earth to be a flat disk. Professor E. P. Wigner, in an

[3] Wien, 1948.

article on 'The Limits of Science'[4] is in doubt whether to date the 'birthyear' of chemistry around 1780 (Lavoisier) or at 1808 (Dalton's law). Physics, he says, is somewhat older, since Newton's *Principia* became available in 1687. He grants that 'Archimedes discovered laws of physics around 250 B.C. but his discoveries can hardly be called the real beginning of physics.' I must not take up space by refuting these strange views, but refer the reader to Professor Benjamin Farrington's two excellent Pelican books on *Greek Science.* Still I would mention that among the 'insignificant' discoveries of that period was the inference, drawn (probably by Archimedes) from the heliocentric system of Aristarchus, that the fixed stars must be at least at a distance of, in our units, about two light years; and the further conclusion that from there the sun would appear as a faint star, and therefore, inversely, many of those stars must equal and even exceed the sun in size—or luminosity, as we would call it today. Of course scientific knowledge takes some time to get a grip on the cultured community. Charles Darwin tells us in the *Voyage of a Naturalist* of the sensation he caused in 1833 among the 'educated' society in Argentina by telling them that the earth is a sphere. This knowledge was then more than 2,300 years old.

What has all this to do with quantum jumps? I have been trying to produce a mood that makes one wonder what parts of contemporary science will still be of interest to others than historians 2,000 years hence. There have been ingenious constructs of the human mind that gave an exceedingly accurate description of observed facts and have yet lost all interest except to historians. I am thinking of the theory of epicycles. I confess to the heretical view that their modern counterpart in physical theory are the quantum jumps. Or rather these correspond to the *circles* which the sun, the moon and the stars were thought to describe around the earth in 24 hours, after earlier and better knowledge had been condemned. I am reminded of *epicycles* of various orders when I am told of the hierarchy of *virtual* quantum transitions. But let

[4] *Proc. Am. Philosoph. Soc.* 1950, 94, 422.

these rude remarks not deter you. We shall now come to grips with the subject proper.

## 2. *The Discontinuous States as Proper Modes*

Max Planck's essential step in 1900, amounted, as we say now, to laying the foundation of quantum theory; it was his discovery, by abstract thought, of a *discontinuity* where it was least expected, namely in the exchange of energy between an elementary material system (atom or molecule) and the radiation of light and heat. He was at first very reluctant to draw the much more incisive conclusion that each atom or molecule had only to choose between a *discrete* set of 'states'; that it could normally only harbour certain discrete amounts of energy, sharply defined and characteristic of its nature; that it would normally find itself on one of these 'energy levels' (as the modern expression runs)—except when it changes over more or less abruptly from one to another, radiating its surplus energy to the environment, or absorbing the required amount from there, as the case may be. Planck was even more hesitant about adopting the view that radiation itself be divided up into portions or light-quanta or 'photons', to use the present terminology. In all this his hesitance had good reasons. Yet only a few years later (1905) Einstein advanced the hypothesis of light-quanta, clinching it with irresistible arguments; and in 1913 Niels Bohr, by taking the discrete states of the atoms seriously and extending Planck's assumptions in two directions with great ingenuity, but irrefutable consistency, could explain quantitatively some of the atomic line spectra, which are all patently *discrete,* and which had in their entirety formed a great conundrum up to then: Bohr's theory turned them into the ultimate and irrevocable direct evidence that the discrete states are a genuine and real fact. Bohr's theory held the ground for about a dozen years, scoring a grand series of such marvellous and genuine successes that we may well claim excuses for having shut our eyes to its one great deficiency: while describing minutely the so-called 'stationary' states which the atom had normally, i.e. in the comparatively uninteresting periods when *nothing happens,* the theory was silent about the periods of transition or 'quantum jumps' (as one then began to call them). Since intermediary states had to remain disallowed, one could not but regard the transition as instantaneous; but on the other hand, the radiating of a coherent wave train of 3 or 4 feet length, as it can be observed in an interferometer, would use up just about the average interval between two transitions, leaving the atom no time to 'be' in those stationary states, the only ones of which the theory gave a description.

This difficulty was overcome by quantum mechanics, more especially by wave mechanics, which furnished a new description of the *states*; this was precisely what was still missing in the earliest version of the new theory which had preceded wave mechanics by about one year. The previously admitted discontinuity was not abandoned, but it shifted from the *states* to something else, which is most easily grasped by the simile of a vibrating string or drumhead or metal plate, or of a bell that is tolling. If such a body is struck, it is set vibrating, that is to say it is slightly deformed and then runs in rapid succession through a continuous series of slight deformations again and again. There is, of course, an infinite variety of ways of striking a given body, say a bell, by a hard or soft, sharp or blunt, instrument, at different points or at several points at a time. This produces an infinite variety of initial deformations and accordingly a truly infinite variety of shapes of the ensuing vibration: the rapid 'succession of cinema pictures', so we might call it, which describes the vibration following on a particular initial deformation is infinitely manifold. But in every case, however complicated the actual motion is, it can be mathematically analysed as being *superposition* of a discrete series of comparatively simple 'proper vibrations', each of which goes on with a quite definite frequency. This discrete series of frequencies depends on the shape and on the material of the body, its density and elastic properties. It can be computed from the theory of elasticity, from which the existence and the discreteness of proper modes and proper frequencies, and the fact that any possible vibration of that body can be analysed into a superposition of them, are very easily deduced quite generally, i.e. for an elastic body of any shape whatsoever.

The achievement of wave mechanics was that it found a general model picture in which the 'stationary' states of Bohr's theory take the role of proper vibrations, and their discrete 'energy levels' the role of the proper frequencies of these proper vibrations; and all this follows from the new theory, once it is accepted, as simply and neatly as in the theory of elastic bodies, which we mentioned as a simile. Moreover, the radiated frequencies, observed in the line spectra, are, in the new model, equal to the *differences* of the proper frequencies; and this is easily understood, when two of them are acting simultaneously, on simple assumptions about the nature of the vibrating 'something'.

## 3. The Alleged Energy Balance—a Resonance Phenomenon

But to me the following point has always seemed the most relevant, and it is the one I wish to stress here, because it has been almost obliterated—if words mean something, and if certain words now in general use are taken to mean what they say. The principle of superposition not only bridges the gaps between the 'stationary' states, and allows, nay, compels, us to admit intermediate states without removing the discreteness of the 'energy levels' (because they have become proper frequencies); but it completely *does away with the prerogative of the stationary states.* The epithet 'stationary' has become obsolete. Nobody who would get acquainted with wave mechanics without knowing its predecessor (the Planck-Einstein-Bohr theory) would be inclined to think that a wave-mechanical system has a predilection for being affected by only one of its proper modes at a time. Yet this is implied by the continued use of the words 'energy levels', 'transitions', 'transition probabilities'.

The perseverance in this way of thinking is understand-

able, because the great and genuine successes of the idea
of energy parcels have made it an ingrained habit to regard the product of Planck's constant $h$ and a frequency
as a bundle of energy, lost by one system and gained by
another. How else should one understand the exact dove-
tailing in the great 'double-entry' book-keeping in nature?
I maintain that it can in all cases be understood as a
resonance phenomenon. One ought at least to try and
look upon atomic frequencies just as frequencies and drop
the idea of energy-parcels. I submit that the word 'energy'
is at present used with two entirely different meanings,
macroscopic and microscopic. Macroscopic energy is a
'quantity-concept' (Quantitätsgrösse). Microscopic energy
(meaning $hv$) is a 'quality-concept' or 'intensity-concept'
(Intensitätsgrösse); it is quite proper to speak of high-
grade and low-grade energy according to the value of the
frequency $v$. True, the macroscopic energy is, strangely
enough, obtained by a certain weighted summation over
the frequencies, and in this relation the constant $h$ is
operative. But this does not necessarily entail that in
every single case of microscopic interaction a whole portion $hv$ of *macroscopic* energy is exchanged. I believe one
is allowed to regard microscopic interaction as a continuous phenomenon without losing either the precious results
of Planck and Einstein on the equlibrium of (macroscopic)
energy between radiation and matter, or any other understanding of phenomena that the parcel-theory affords.

The one thing which one has to accept and which is the
inalienable consequence of the wave-equation as it is used
in every problem, under the most various forms, is this:
that the interaction between two microscopic physical
systems is controlled by a peculiar law of resonance. This
law requires that the *difference* of two proper frequencies
of the one system be equal to the difference of two proper
frequencies of the other:

$$v_1 - v_1' = v_2' - v_2. \qquad (I)$$

The interaction is appropriately described as a gradual
change of the amplitudes of the four proper vibrations
in question. People have kept to the habit of multiplying

this equation by $h$, and saying it means that the first system (index I) has dropped from the energy level $hv_1$ to the level $hv_1'$, the balance being transferred to the second system, enabling it to rise from $hv_2$ to $hv_2'$. This interpretation is obsolete. There is nothing to recommend it, and it bars the understanding of what is actually going on. It obstinately refuses to take stock of the principle of superposition, which enables us to envisage simultaneous gradual changes of any and all amplitudes without surrendering the essential discontinuity, if any, namely that of the frequencies. To be accurate we must add that the condition of resonance, equation (I), may include three or more interacting systems. It may for example read

$$v_1 - v_1' = v_2' - v_2 + v_3' - v_3. \tag{2}$$

Moreover we may adopt the view that the two or more interacting systems are regarded as *one* system. One is then inclined to write equations (I) and (2), respectively, as follows

$$v_1 + v_2 = v_1' + v_2' \tag{I'}$$
$$v_1 + v_2 + v_3 = v_1' + v_2' + v_3', \tag{2'}$$

and to state the resonance condition thus: the interaction is restricted to constituent vibrations of the *same* frequency. This is a familiar state of affairs, of old. Unfamiliar is the tacit admission that frequencies are *additive*, when two or more systems are considered as forming *one* system. It is an inevitable consequence of wave mechanics. Is it so very repugnant to common sense? If I smoke 25 cigarettes per day, and my wife smokes 10, and my daughter 12—is not the family consumption 47 per day—on the average?

### 4. *A Typical Experiment*

Jokes aside, I wish to consider some typical experiments that ostensibly force the energy-parcel view upon us, and I wish to show that this is an illusion. A beam of cathode rays of uniform velocity, which can be gradually increased, is passed through sodium vapour. Behind the vessel containing the vapour the beam passes an electric field which deflects it and tells us the velocity of the particles after the passage. At the same time a spectrometer inspects the light, if any, emitted by the vapour. For small initial velocity nothing happens: no light, no change of velocity in the cathode beam. But when the initial velocity is increased beyond a sharply defined limit, two things happen. The vapour begins to glow, radiating the frequency of the first line of the 'principal series'; and the beam of cathode rays emerging from the vapour is split into two by the deflecting electric field, one indicating the initial velocity unchanged, and another slow one has 'lost an amount of energy' equal to the frequency of the said spectral line multiplied by Planck's constant $h$. If the velocity is further increased the story repeats itself when the incident cathode ray energy increases beyond the 'energy level' that is responsible for the second line (or rather the 'level-difference' in question); this line appears and a third beam of cathode rays with correspondingly reduced speed occurs; and so on. This was, and still is, regarded as blatant evidence of the energy-parcel view.[5]

But it is just as easily understood from the resonance point of view. A cathode ray of particles with uniform velocity is a monochromatic beam of de Broglie waves. Only when its frequency ($v_1$) surpasses the frequency difference ($v_2' - v_2$) between the lowest ($v_2$) and the second ($v_2'$) proper frequencies of the sodium atom, is there a de Broglie frequency $v_1' > 0$ that fulfils the resonance demand, equation (I). Then the vibration $v_1'$ appears in the de Broglie wave and $v_2'$ among the atoms which begin to glow with frequency $v_2' - v_2$, since Max-

[5] Professor Michael Polanyi has drawn my attention to a mistake. My description of the Franck-Hertz experiment in this paragraph is, to put it mildly, oversimplified. The cathode ray beam is appreciably scattered in the vapour. The two or more electronic frequencies that emerge could therefore hardly be separated by the simple transversal field method. But any two of them can be separated by a potential barrier which the one can penetrate, while the other is turned back, being totally reflected. Since this is also completely understood by de Broglie's wave equation, the main argument is not impaired.

well's 'electromagnetic vacuum' is prepared for resonance with anything. The splitting of the cathode ray beam in the deviating electric field, after passing the vapour, is accounted for by de Broglie's wave equation. An electric field has for de Broglie waves an 'index of refraction' that *depends* on their frequency ('dispersion') and has a gradient in the direction of the field (which thus acts as an 'inhomogeneous medium'). Any further events that might happen, for instance a transfer of some of the 'energy quanta' $h(v_2' - v_2)$ from the sodium atoms to other gas molecules by 'impacts of the second kind', are just as easily understood as resonance phenomena, provided only one keeps to the wave picture throughout and for all particles involved.

Many similar cases of apparent transfer of energy-parcels can be reduced to resonance—for instance photochemical action. The pattern is always the same: you may either take equations like (I) or (2) as they stand (resonance), or multiply them by $h$ and think they express an energy balance of every single micro-transition. In the preceding example one point is of particular interest. One is able by an external agent (the electric field) to *separate in space* the two or more frequencies which have arisen in the cathode ray by the interaction; for they behave differently towards this agent, and the different behaviour is completely understood from de Broglie's wave equation; one thus obtains two or more beams of homogeneous frequency (or velocity). It is extremely valuable that there are simple cases of this kind in which the separation into two 'phases' has nothing enigmatic; it is an immediate consequence of the principles laid down in L. de Broglie's earliest work on material waves. I say, this is fortunate; for there is a vast domain of phenomena in which the separation in space either takes place in the natural conditions of observation, or can easily be brought about by simple appliances; but it is not as easily explained on first principles. This might dishearten one in accepting the view of gradually changing amplitudes that I put forward here; for the separation into different phases that produces itself before our eyes seems to confirm the belief that a discontinuous abrupt and *complete* transition occurs in every single microscopic interaction.

## 5. *Chemistry, Photochemistry, and the Photoelectric Effect*

The vast amount of phenomena I am alluding to is in the first place ordinary chemistry. Two or more constituents, mixed in a solution or in a gaseous phase, begin to react with each other, under the influence of light or otherwise; the portions that have reacted and have formed a new chemical compound may separate themselves almost entirely from the rest and form a new phase, say because the product is almost insoluble in the liquid, or (in the case of a gaseous mixture) by its being a liquid or solid with a low vapour pressure at the temperature in question. Almost any chemical reaction may serve as an example, but let us take a slow one to facilitate speech and thought. If a suitable mixture of hydrogen gas ($H_2$) and oxygen gas ($O_2$) is illuminated by ultraviolet light, the following slow reaction is induced

$$2H_2 + O_2 \rightarrow 2H_2O \qquad (3)$$

As the concentration of water vapour ($H_2O$) increases, part of it separates off into liquid droplets.

The actual process is not as simple as the balance (3) indicates; it is a chain reaction. But we need pay no attention to this, and contemplate only the initial state and the end-product. Wave-mechanically the gaseous mixture is represented by a vibration of the combined system, and, by the way, not by *one* proper vibration since there is anyhow the vast variety of translational and rotational modes, and, of course, the electronic modes. The gaseous compound, $H_2O$, is represented by an entirely different vibration of the *same* system. The modes composing it, absent at first, are gradually chiming in as the reaction proceeds. But then there is a *third* group of vibrations representing the liquid $H_2O$; they gradually build up where they are facilitated by dust nuclei, and are observed as droplets. It is, of course, deplorable that wave mechanics does not allow us to follow this *observed* process analytically, while, in the now current interpretation, ample information is forthcoming about a host of experiments that nobody has ever been or ever will be able to perform (for instance we are told, what is the probability of our finding at a definite spot inside a given hydrogen atom an electron, if we look for one). But there is no reason to suspect that the separation of phases is fundamentally different from the spectroscopic resolution of a beam of light or of cathode rays into its monochromatic constituents. One need not be afraid that the formation of spatial boundaries, separating coherent regions of chemically or physically distinct properties, cannot possibly be controlled by the wave equation, but must necessarily be accounted for by the picturesque pageantry of individual molecules swallowing or respewing whole energy parcels, being disrupted and recombined, until they eventually go to form one or two molecules of a new type.

I deem the latter simply wrong; it is not in accordance with our present state of knowledge, whose further progress is hampered if these easy pictures, that are in common use, are taken literally. And we are encouraged to take them literally not only by text-books and popular essays but also by the language used in very high-browed technical treatises. By this I will not deny that this imagery is a very useful, nay, indispensable, conceptual shorthand in chemical research. One cannot see how to avoid it when, for example, a complicated chain reaction is to be unravelled. And, of course, the chemical equation for describing a reaction will never be ousted, though it ostensibly describes the single micro-event and is wrong in this. It is an instance of the famous 'as if'. It is not the first instance of this kind in the relation of chemistry and physics. The chemist used the valency stroke for building models of complicated molecules. It represented very real facts of observation. For a long time the physicist could not supply any explanation of the mechanism of the chemical bond. Then, in quick succession, *two* were given: there is a heteropolar bond (Kossel, 1916) and a homopolar bond (London-Heitler, 1926). The discoveries were illuminating to the chemist, indeed they removed some difficulties caused by interpreting the valency strokes too naïvely. But, of course, the valency strokes were retained as an extremely convenient shorthand. They could be retained because they were based on carefully pondered observation.

As one of the simplest photochemical reactions we may regard the photoelectric effect, which was one of the main incentives for Einstein in 1905 to launch the hypothesis of light quanta. When a metal plate is illuminated by light of sufficiently high *frequency,* electrons emerge from it forthwith with an energy corresponding to this frequency. There is no time delay, even when the *intensity* of the incident light is so weak that according to the electron theory of H. A. Lorentz, which was at the time in full swing, an electron would need half an hour to be sped up to the velocity in question. This was—and, I am afraid, still is—regarded as convincing evidence of the instantaneous transfer of whole quanta of energy from the light to the electron. I understand the present orthodox interpretation to be as follows. The incident light beam produces at once in each of tens of thousands of electrons an exceedingly small *probability* of taking within the next split second a leap into a state of higher translational energy; a correspondingly small fraction of those tens of thousands do so and emerge from the metal, and that is why the game starts without delay.

But according to wave mechanics, as put forward by de Broglie and myself and generally accepted, the interpretation does produce without delay electronic wave trains of the higher frequency that we observe emerging from the metal. (For to observe the *frequency* of an electron or its *velocity* means the same thing.) After this has been recognized, is the probability scheme any longer needed? Has the idea of the mysterious sudden leaps of single electrons not become gratuitous? Is it expedient? The waves are there anyhow, and we are not at a loss to prove it. We need only put a tube of crystal powder in the way of the emerging beam and produce an interference pattern of the type first achieved by G. P. Thomson (it might not be as beautiful as Thomson's, but it would vouch for the waves all the same).

## 6. *Single Interaction Processes between Micro-Systems ('Collisions')*

There are besides chemistry several other domains of theoretical investigation in which the simplifying scheme of individual constituent micro-systems on sharp energy levels, with abrupt transitions between them, affords a very convenient shorthand. Nearly all thermodynamical considerations are greatly facilitated by adopting this scheme in speech and thought, which makes very little difference, if any, in the results. This constitutes a certain danger. In the inseparable union of speech and thought the primacy, rather paradoxically, rests with speech. When we hear the same words again and again pronounced with authority, we are apt to forget that they were originally meant as an abbreviation; we are induced to believe that they describe a reality.

If the simplified scheme of sharp energy states and abrupt transitions between them was workable throughout in all instances (which I do not think is the case), one would have to try and cast it into a consistent theory. At the moment no such theory exists and I can see no prospect of obtaining one, nor any inducement to try, for the reason just mentioned in parenthesis. At present the scheme is inconsistent, not only because of the mystery the *transitions* continue to present from their first appearance in the theories of Planck (1900) and Bohr (1913), but also for another reason, intimately connected with the former. In application to two individual micro-systems which interact, it is not at all clear which are the pure energy levels distinguished, to which the scheme shall apply. The choice rests with the mathematical technique. The usual procedure is as follows. The total energy (which enters the mathematical analysis as the 'operator' of the wave equation) is regarded as made up of three additive parts; the two main contributions are said to pertain to the single systems and are said to control their behaviours, respectively, if they did *not* interact; the third is said to be their energy (or 'operator') of interaction. But this partition is rather artificial, at any rate whilst the interaction takes place. It is largely guided by the requirement that the main parts should be comparatively simple and easy to deal with analytically, the whole complication of the problem being shoved into the interaction, which is called a perturbation and dealt with by methods of approximation. Even so, it is hardly ever amenable to a true solution (albeit an approximate one); one has to content oneself with finding out what happens in a small interval of time. One computes the very small changes of amplitudes that occur during this short interval; and one is pleased to call the time-rate of change the *probability of transition*. By calling it so one expresses the belief that after the interaction has taken place and the two systems have separated again each of them will find itself in a pure sharp energy state. The computation does *not* give this result. The computation tells us that in either system a host of pure energy-states will be superposed—with a certain dependence between the partial amplitudes in the one system and those in the other. But one chooses to interpret this result as meaning that there will be *complete* exchange between only *one* pair of proper modes, one of the many for which the resonance condition holds.

One might say, why not, if this interpretation works and if it is consistent? I maintain that it is inconsistent. The reason is the following. Assume each of the two systems found itself in a pure energy state, when they were isolated, before the interaction started. Now let the interaction set in; take it to be very weak. It is certainly legitimate to adopt the attitude that we are now faced with *one* system; nay, this is the fundamentally correct attitude to take; the splitting of the wave-operator ('energy') into two private parts plus a part depicting the interaction is only a mathematical artifice. But however weak the interaction be, it has the *immediate* consequence that the combined system is now very far from any one of *its* pure energy states. This is not the result of a very strong mutual physical influence. It obtains prior to any physical change. It results from a slight distuning of the proper modes by the perturbation. What were clear 'one tone' proper modes in the isolated systems no longer are in the combined 'dis-tuned' systems—*not nearly*. You have to reshuffle them and combine (superpose) them *in your mind* in an intriguing fashion to find the proper modes of the combined system. I say 'in your mind'—there is, of course, no immediate physical reshuffling; you just state that your combined system is very far from finding itself in one of its proper modes. And that is the very reason why, as time goes on, anything will happen at all, and why, in fact, even a weak interaction, given time, will produce substantial changes of the amplitudes. For it is a simple elementary and universally recognized statement of wave mechanics that an isolated system that vibrates exactly in one of its proper modes undergoes no change whatsoever.

This has, by the way, a consequence worth mentioning. When we spoke just before of a weak interaction setting in between the previously isolated systems, the reader may very naturally have pictured to himself the two systems being first at great distance and then approaching each other and getting in contact. I avoided this description on purpose, because it would flatly contradict the assumption that the isolated systems were in pure energy states. *If so they cannot be said to approach each other.* To think of atoms and molecules *in pure energy states* moving hither and thither, colliding and rebounding, contradicts the fundamental concepts of the theory. Where anything *happens*, we are not facing pure energy states. So obviously we never are.

Let me return for a moment to our two micro-systems in weak interaction or, as I prefer to say, to a system consisting of two parts in slight coupling. The state of affairs is simply this: if this system as a whole settled down in one of its exact proper modes, this would *not* be a state which *the current view* interprets as indicating a definite partition of the total energy between the two parts—*not nearly*; I mean to say, it is not a question of slight fluctuation or uncertainty, but of many widely different partitions. If you abolished the coupling at this moment, the now isolated parts would vibrate, each of them, in a superposition of *widely* different proper modes.

Summarizing: the current view, which privileges the 'sharp energy states', is self-contradictory, at least in the language it uses (what people mean, when they say something else than they mean, is difficult to guess). We found it self-contradictory in that it cannot be maintained for both the whole and the parts; we are left to choose and to apply the privilege the way it is most convenient. We found a minor inconsistency in the apparently innocent statement that two systems (both of sharply defined energy) *approach* each other and collide. This seems a little less obnoxious, because it can be evaded by saying: Oh well, we do not mean really quite sharp. Some may consider this point a rather gratuitous nagging. I wonder whether in actual collision problems it is entirely irrelevant.

## 7. The Cultural Background, Again

It might be maintained that the case I am making in this essay is quite irrelevant. It might be said that the 'privilege' is not meant seriously, that I am naïvely taking it at its face value. We may, so my opponent might continue, use the pure energy states of *any* system; just take our choice so that they are convenient to handle analytically. Any state of any system may be regarded as some superposition of some or all of its proper modes (= pure energy states). One may deal with them separately, *as if* the system was in one of them; the several results, duly superposed, will then tell us what would come of their superposition, if we really want to know. Perhaps my supposed opponent would even grant that he is using just a convenient shorthand, the same as in chemistry and statistical thermodynamics; but he would maintain that this is perfectly admissible also for investigating a single event of interaction between micro-systems.

To this I have two answers, referring to two very

different points. The first is this. Even if this shorthand were admissible for the micro-event, we have to keep in mind that physicists are not the only people interested in physics and in the outcome of theoretical research in physics. Those results that are tenable and will survive are destined, eventually, to be absorbed into our world-picture and to become part and parcel thereof. A great many of our educated contemporaries, not equipped with the mathematical apparatus to follow our more technical deliveries, are yet deeply concerned with many general questions; one of the most stirring among them certainly is whether actually *natura facit saltus* or no. Whatever abbreviated language we physicists may find convenient to use among ourselves, we ought to be aware of the dilemmas that justly and duly interest others; we must be careful not to veil or distort them by indulging in loose speech. It is this point that I had in mind in my general historical introduction. Science is not a soliloquy. It gains value only within its cultural milieu, only by having contact with all those who are now, and who in future will be, engaged in promoting spiritual culture and knowledge. The extant scientific papers of Archimedes, the dialogues and discourses of Galileo, are still of genuine interest in our day, and not only to philologists, but to many scientists. Would it mean setting ourselves too high and too proud a goal, if we occasionally thought of what will have become of our scientific papers 2,000 years hence? Science will have changed entirely. Will there be anybody to grasp our meaning, as we grasp the meaning of Archimedes?

## 8. *Details about Collisions*

This was the first part of my answer to the supposed opponent. The second part is more technical, and ought to be supported by a little mathematics which I must avoid here. I doubt whether in dealing with a micro-event ('collision problem') one is allowed to pick one's 'initial state' arbitrarily as composed of pure energy states of the two non-interacting systems, relying on the principle of untainted superposition. In point of fact, this procedure regularly leads to very acceptable results in the first meaningful approximation and to entirely unacceptable ones in the next step of approximation. Now it so happens that in the wave equation the term that depicts the inter-action (engendered by that relatively small third part of the energy operator which we spoke of in Section 5), is, of necessity, a *non-linear* term; it must contain the *product of the two wave-functions,* otherwise it could not entail any interaction between them. Thus by the very task it has to fulfill this term must infringe upon linearity, and thereby do away with clean and simple superposition. And it is, of course, from this term, and from this term alone, that the results are deduced. Now general mathe-matical considerations tell us in a case of this kind, three things, namely

(i) starting from any initial situation, the first small change caused by the perturbating term is cor-rectly computed from the latter in spite of its non-linearity; but

(ii) the changes computed in this way for two or more initial situations are not simply additive, when an initial situation, composed of the former, is con-templated; there is a substantial mutual influence of the components; moreover

(iii) to improve on the first approximation is a very intricate task, if the perturbing term is not linear; the current routine follows, as far as I can see, the pattern introduced for *linear* perturbations. Thus it is insufficient to cover the actual situation.

There may, of course, be other reasons for the actual failure of the approximation method, a failure now usually referred to as 'the divergences'. We have loosely called the interaction operator 'relatively small'. Now this epithet cannot properly apply to an operator, only to the quantity which results from applying the operator to another quan-tity (in our case: to the wave-functions). This result is different in different parts of the field. There may be regions where the 'relative smallness' does not hold. It may be justifiable to disregard this fact, and the approximation method may none the less yield acceptable results. Even so one must be prepared to discover a fundamental shortcoming. This is well illustrated by the first application of this method of approximation, leading to the earliest quantitative achievement of wave mechanics, viz. my computation, in 1926, of the splitting of the spectral lines of atomic hydrogen by an external electric field (Stark effect). Both the frequencies and the intensities agreed very satisfactorily with observation. Yet a few years later Cornel Lanczos discovered a fundamental shortcoming in my statements. Compared with the field of the nucleus, the perturbing external field is weak only in the neighbourhood of the nucleus, where the internal field is strong; the ratio is reversed at moderate distances, since the internal field fades away rapidly according to the inverse square law while the external field is constant. This has the consequence that none of the Stark effect lines is really sharp, an effect that is readily observed in the higher members of the spectral series when a fairly strong external field is applied.

There is another point that I consider relevant in collision problems. Towards the end of Section 6 I mentioned that two micro-systems which vibrate, each of them truly and exactly in one of its proper modes, cannot be conceived as approaching each other. This is not a far-fetched subtlety. Translatory motion with precisely fixed velocity is wave-mechanically represented by a plane sinusoidal wave filling the whole space. Two such plane waves, one pertaining to the first, the other to the second, system do not exhibit any feature representing 'distance from each other'. They describe a state that virtually includes all possible distances down to the smallest at which the interaction already is 'in full swing'. To choose for the *initial state* one that includes these two plane waves seems hazardous. One thereby disregards the building up of the interaction during the gradual approach. I am more surprised at the acceptable results this procedure yields in the first instance than at its ensuing failure. Sometimes it is permissible to think of one system as localized. One would then at least have to picture the other as a plane wave *with a wave head* or wave front, approaching the point where the collision is to take place. It is known from pre-quantum physics that what happens at a wave front may differ widely from the stationary state that establishes itself by and by in its rear. For example, it was shown by A. Sommerfeld that when a plane electro-magnetic wave passes from vacuum into a dielectric (pictured as composed of molecules that contain elec-tronic oscillators), the head of the wave is not refracted according to Snell's law, but continues indefinitely in the same direction with unchanged velocity of propagation. The reason is that the electrons are initially at rest; each of them is seized upon by the oncoming wave train and is gradually rocked into oscillations of increasing ampli-tude until an equilibrium state is reached after many waves have passed. True, this model is obsolete. But the means used now to depict the physical situation still fol-low the pattern to which it belonged. I do not believe that the intricacies involved in the 'classical' problems have passed away. I find it hard to believe that quantum physics holds the master key for overcoming these intrica-cies without attacking them. In the above example, taken from Lorentzian electronics, the initial state, which shows us an undisturbed incident wave and an electron at rest, differs very substantially from the final state, when the electron is in full swing and superposes its wavelet on the incident wave. (Indeed, all these wavelets together turn the original plane wave into one of entirely different velocity and entirely different direction.) In Lorentzian electronics this gradual transition cannot possibly be dealt with as a problem of 'perturbation'. One cannot hope that in quantum physics this method will yield an exhaustive answer, unless one maintains that according to quantum physics nothing of the sort happens at all, and that the whole analytical apparatus is set up only for telling us with what probability the system may choose to hop from one state into another, these 'states' being patently selected so as to meet our analytical convenience and ability. Is that not wishful thinking?

### 9.  *On Neo-Machian Purism*

There is, of course, among physicists a widely popular tenet, informed by the philosophy of Ernst Mach, to the effect that the only task of experimental science is to give definite *prescriptions* for successfully foretelling the results of any future observations from the known results of previous observations. If this contention is taken at its face value, then *not only* is it irrelevant whether the prescription makes use of a visualized model or only consists in definitely prescribed mathematical operations, to be performed with the previously observed values in order to obtain predicted values; *but also* the said operations would apparently not even have to be mathematically correct, as long as they are precise and enable us to prophesy correctly. Indeed the lack of rigour in a theoretical deduction is nowadays sometimes followed by the remark that what vindicates the procedure is its success, its leading to results that agree with observation. The neo-Machian principle covers this argument not only pending the proof that the theoretical deduction is correct, *but even if it should prove to be wrong.*

Nobody will agree. But why? If our task is only to predict precisely and correctly by any means whatsoever, why not by false mathematics? Because as little as in any other science does the scientific method in physics consist of a vast number of juxtaposed independent prescriptions for the purpose of prophecy. Whether or no they are based on a visualizable model-picture, those prescriptions, if one wants to give them this abstract name, form an intricately connected and interwoven scheme. Even in the simplest quantitative experiment, half a dozen of them must be relied upon for applying corrections to the rough numbers read on the scales, before you obtain what you call the result of your measurement. Moreover, there are basic statements or assumptions, from which a thousand branches of inference issue, which coalescing in bundles with many others eventually lead off and on to a relevant new 'prediction.' And in every single experiment, though it be not of a new type, this network of inferences has to be produced afresh, adapted to the special data and circumstances. The 'scheme of prescriptions' is not satisfactory unless we trust it to embrace, suitably applied, *any* future observation. We have no other means for rendering tolerably precise the application to new cases that were not foreseen, any, for drawing any conclusions at all with respect to them, but to decide once and for all to use the self-consistent scheme of correct mathematics. Mathematics is not a very special thing. It is the most general way of contemplating the possible relationships between numbers without contradiction. A single 'formula', provided it contains at least one undetermined symbol (and does not exhibit an explicit zero as a denominator), cannot be 'mathematically wrong'. Those 'prescriptions' of physical science contain at least two undetermined symbols, viz. at least one representing a previous observation, and one that is to be predicted. So no single prescription can be mathematically wrong. But we have never to do with one alone. We have to combine them in rational thought. Without a guide we should be groping in the dark. Correct mathematics is the indispensable guide even to the hardiest Machian purist. Most physicists, whether or no they confess to it, are using some kind of model-picture besides.

So much for vindicating my clamour for mathematical consistency in handling collision problems.

## 10. *Numbers*

The states of sharp energy (whose privilege of being *the* states of a system, with abrupt transitions between them, I contest) include the characteristic that the total number of particles of every kind contained in the system be an integer. According to Einstein's famous discovery (1905) that mass and energy are the same thing, a particle of rest-mass $m$, when at rest, represents an amount of energy $mc^2$ ($c$ = velocity of light in vacuo). Broadly speaking, $n$ equal particles contained in a system contribute the amount $nmc^2$ to any of the sharp energy levels of the whole system, which differ therefore on this account by integral multiples of $mc^2$. This is an entirely sound, nay, an unavoidable assumption, even though we have not yet succeeded in accounting satisfactorily for the various numerical values of $m$ actually observed in the various elementary particles, as electrons, protons, the various mesons, etc., from which the masses of atoms and molecules are composed.

From the point of view taken here we must consider it inadequate to think, e.g., of a body of nitrogen gas in front of us as consisting of a definite integral number of nitrogen molecules that could be indicated. It has to be represented by a superposition of proper modes with a considerable spread over many integers. We should wish to estimate the extension of this spread. This, it must be granted, is not so easy. Though it is *not* a question of fluctuations, one naturally thinks that considerations of the kind used in thermodynamics might come to our rescue. However, the thermal energy of one degree of freedom ($\frac{1}{2}kT$) is—except perhaps at the temperature $T$ of the interior of a star—so small compared with the rest energies $mc^2$, that in ordinary circumstances no system containing ponderable mass must be considered in *true* thermodynamic equilibrium.

The following attempt to answer the question suggests itself. Our isolated body of nitrogen gas has the same properties as one that forms part of a much larger body from which it is only severed by fictitious boundaries; indeed our body might have been obtained from a much larger one, the fictitious boundaries being replaced by real ones. It is universally agreed that the number $N$ of molecules contained within a volume delimited only in thought exhibits fluctuations of the order of $\sqrt{N}$. I consider it reasonable to assume that the wave function of the isolated system would in general be composed of eigenfunctions whose $N$-values spread over a region of order of magnitude $\sqrt{N}$.

It may be asked: what difference does this make? Could it be tested by experiment? The main difference is that it is reasonable, while it is unreasonable to admit a sharp count of $N$ of objects that avowedly lack individuality.[6] Secondly, this is the obvious way of registering the fact that we *never* experiment with just *one* electron or atom or (small) molecule. In thought-experiments we sometimes assume that we do; this invariably entails ridiculous consequences as, e.g., that a spherical de Broglie wave, which is supposed to represent 'one' electron, moving in an 'unknown' direction, suddenly collapses into a small wave parcel, when 'that' electron is detected at a definite spot. Nothing of the sort happens if the number 'one' is not ascertained, but may as well be zero or two or three. Even better: the certain detection of one does not reduce the expectation of a second or third, it leaves it unchanged, according to generally accepted principles of statistics. And, I do not regret to say, we sorely need those spherical waves as realities (not merely as expressing our lack of knowledge), if we wish to account, e.g., for G. P. Thomson's beautiful experiments on the interference patterns of de Broglie waves diffracted by crystals; and the same in many, many other cases.

## 11. *Observing Single Particles*

In writing this I have before me the lovely records of single particle tracks, of 'stars' (nuclear disintegrations), of 'showers', of broken tracks showing successive decays of one particle ($\tau \to \mu \to e$), the photographic emulsion records that C. F. Powell selected to illustrate his Nobel lecture on cosmic radiation in 1950. I am asking myself whether here as well as in the tracks of particles produced in the Wilson cloud chamber we are not actually experimenting with a quite definite number of particles, in some cases really with just one particle, and whether we are not presented with records of quantum transitions, which I am so anxious to deny.

In the first place it is fair to state that we are not *experimenting* with single particles, any more than we can raise

---

[6] The lack of individuality of micro-systems is argued in my article in *Endeavour*, July 1950, 9, No. 35; reprinted in the Smithsonian Report for 1950, pp. 183–96; in German, *Die Pyramide*, January and February, 1951.

Ichthyosauria in the zoo. We are scrutinizing records of events long after they have happened. That the interval of time is shorter, and that we have ourselves produced favourable conditions for the records to produce themselves, makes no difference. We can never reproduce the same single-particle-event under planned varied conditions; and this is the typical procedure of the experimenter.

But now to the other question: are these not records of quantum transitions? They certainly do *not* show us the transformation of a couple of plane waves (representing the colliding particles before the collision) into a number of other plane waves (representing the particles that emerge after the collision). Here my opponent interrupts me: 'Well, that's just the point. That is why your waves must not be regarded themselves as a real observable phenomenon, but only as indicating the probability of particle-phenomena.' I mentioned just before that there are many experiments which we simply cannot account for without taking the wave to be a wave, acting simultaneously throughout the region over which it spreads, not 'perhaps here' or 'perhaps there', as the probability view would have it. I shall come back to this point.

The real difficulty for the wave aspect is the exact balance of energy (and momentum) *in the single event*, for which the said records (in the photographic plate and in the Wilson cloud chamber) are full evidence. Take the simplest case: an alpha-particle of given initial velocity in the cloud-chamber. It has a well defined range; it is always stopped after travelling a distance of, say, 5 cms., and after producing a certain number of ionizations, which number is practically always the same and corresponds to the particle spending its kinetic energy and coming to rest. How are we to understand this, if ionization is to mean *not* the transfer of an energy parcel, but only a resonance phenomenon? Well, there would be no difficulty in understanding it, if the slowing down were due to a static gravitational or electric field against which the particle runs up. In this case, if we picture the particle as a composite wave-phenomenon (usually called a 'wave parcel'), this would, according to the theory, actually be slowed down as a whole and come to rest as a whole, always at the same distance, when its 'kinetic energy is spent.' What happens is that all the constituents have their wave-length slowly, 'adiabatically', increased so that the group keeps together. To meet the actual case we are speaking of, one has to adopt the view that the ionizable medium influences the particle that passes through it in the same adiabatic fashion as a field would. I cannot see that this view is quite unacceptable once we have shaken off the nightmare that physical events consist in continual sequences of little fits and jerks, the handing over of energy parcels from one particle (or group of particles) to another.

I believe that not even the apparently catastrophic events oblige us to accept the 'fit and jerk view'; I mean the events recorded as 'stars' showing a nucleus shelled to pieces by the impact of a swift particle. They only occur with *exceedingly* fast particles of *exceedingly* high wave frequency. This encourages one to think that they too may be slow, adiabatic processes; for the criterion of 'slowness' always is: slow compared with the rapidly oscillating wave-field. One has, of course, to use the auxiliary concept, familiar to quantum physicists, of wave parcels in more than three dimensions, actually three times the number of particles that come into play. To enlarge on this here in general terms would have little value. Besides I am quite aware that eventually there remains the momentous question: what are these apparent particles anyhow? Can it be understood that they turn up within continuous wave trains—somewhat like the white crests in a choppy sea— and that in some cases they constitute the only observable features of these wave trains?

I am aware of these questions. They are no longer as embarrassing as they were, before we had gained the insight we have now gained into what a particle certainly is *not*; it is *not* a durable little thing with individuality.[7] However, let me conceive of an opponent to whom the preceding paragraphs of this Section 11 seem lame excuses and loose talk. To him I should still plead as follows.

[7] See my article in *Endeavour*, July 1950, 9, No. 35.

The cloud-chamber and emulsion phenomena, though they are at the moment in the focus of interest, represent after all only a small section of all that we know about nature. In their apparent simplicity they appeal to the vivid imagination of an intelligent child. They would have set any of the old warriors for the cause of atomism, from Democritus down to Dalton and Boltzmann, gasping with joyful excitement. Yet they are not as simple as they look. This is witnessed by the pages and pages of intricate formalism that are often devoted to accounting for even the simplest of them. We must not be so rash as to remove the obvious difficulties presented by these new and unprecedented observations, by remodelling our picture of the physical world in a manner that makes it unfit to give us an understanding of a great many other things that are at the moment not fashionable.

To give an example: if one scans the introductory chapters of Max von Laue's standard works on the diffraction of X-rays[8] and on the diffraction of material waves,[9] one finds that no pattern of thought has yet been discovered to get on in these matters even one step without regarding the wave-functions—Maxwell's field and the de Broglie amplitudes of both the incident wave and those it encounters in the diffracting body—as describing something real. Here 'real' is not a controversial philosophical term. It means that the wave acts simultaneously throughout the whole region it covers, not either here or there. That would fail to account for the interference phenomena. So the epithet 'real' means the momentous difference between 'both-and' (*et-et*) and 'either-or' (*aut-aut*). I challenge anyone to dispute this discrepancy away, if he can. I do not think there is any escape from this: if you accept the current probability view (*aut-aut*) in quantum mechanics, the single-event observation becomes comparatively easy to tackle, but all the rest of physics (unfashionable at the moment) is lost to sight.

[8] *Roentgenstrahlinterferenzen*, Berlin, Akad. Verl. Ges., 1941.
[9] *Materiewellen und ihre Interferenzen*, ibid., 1948.

# Our Conception of Matter

## 1. The Crisis. Preview

The title of this lecture (in its French version) was suggested to me by the committee. I gladly accepted it. But before I try to do it justice as well as I can, I must point out *two* things. *First*, the physicist of to-day can no longer within his field of research significantly distinguish between matter and something else. We no longer contrast matter with forces and fields of force as different entities, we know now that these concepts have to be merged. It is true, we call a spatial region free of matter, call it empty if there is nothing but a gravitational field. But space is never really empty because even far away in the universe there is starlight, and that *is* matter. Besides, according to Einstein, gravity and inertia are of the same nature and therefore cannot very well be separated. Our subject to-day is thus in fact the total picture of space-time reality as envisaged by physics.

The *second* point is this: This picture of material reality is to-day more wavering and uncertain than it has been for a long time. We know a great many interesting details, learn new ones every week. But to seek out among the basic ideas those which are actually established and to construct out of them a clear, easily comprehensible framework of which could it be said: This is unquestionably the way things are, this we all believe to-day—that is simply impossible. A widely accepted school of thought maintains that an objective picture of reality—in any traditional meaning of that term—cannot exist at all. Only the optimists among us (and I consider myself one of them) look upon this view as a philosophical extravagance born of despair in the face of a grave crisis. We hope that the fluctuations of concepts and opinions only indicate a violent process of transformation which in the end will lead to something better than the mess of formulas that to-day surrounds our subject.

It is for me—and also for you, the audience—rather embarrassing that the picture of matter that I am supposed to draw before you does not yet exist, but only fragments exist of more or less partial truth value. As a result one cannot avoid in such a narrative contradicting at a later time what one has said before; like Cervantes, who lets Sancho Panza lose the darling little donkey on which he rides, but a few chapters later the author has forgotten about it and the dear animal is back again. To escape a similar reproach I shall sketch a brief campaign plan. I shall report later on how Max Planck discovered, more than fifty years ago, that energy is only transferred in quanta, i.e., in indivisible portions the size of which is well-determined in each particular case. But since Einstein proved soon afterwards the identity of energy and mass, we must acknowledge that the long familiar ultimate material particles, the atoms or corpuscles whose existence is nowadays quite 'tangibly' demonstrated by many beautiful experiments, are also energy quanta, and we must, so to speak, date back Planck's discovery by more than 2,000 years. It thus appears the more firmly ascertained. Here, it will be in order to take a glance at the enormous significance of this discreteness or *countability* of all that is and that happens, because only thus can Boltzmann's famous statistical theory of the *irreversible* course of nature be carried out and clearly understood.

This is all very well and has certainly high truth value. But then Sancho Panza's donkey will return—after more than 2,000 years. For I shall have to ask you to believe neither in corpuscles as permanent individuals nor in the suddenness of the transfer of an energy quantum from one carrier to another. Discreteness is present, but not in the traditional sense of discrete single particles, let alone in the sense of abrupt processes. This would contradict other well-established evidence. Discreteness arises merely as a structure from the laws governing the phenomena. These laws are by no means as yet fully understood; a probably correct analogue from the physics of palpable bodies is the way various partial tones of a bell derive from its shape and from the laws of elasticity, to which, of themselves, nothing discontinuous adheres.

## 2. Some remarks on corpuscles

Let us start. The idea that matter is made up of ultimate particles was advanced as early as the 5th century B.C. by Leucippus and Democritus, who called these particles atoms. By the turn of the last century, this idea had taken quite definite shape as the *corpuscular theory* of matter—extending to interesting details—and during the first decade of our century it was further clarified and solidified. To sketch, however briefly, all the beautiful, fundamentally important individual discoveries obtained on the way, I should have to occupy your attention for two hours. The start had been made by chemistry. Even to-day, some minds cannot yet get rid of the idea that chemistry is the very own domain of 'atoms' and 'molecules'. From the very hypothetical and somewhat bloodless role these particles played there—Ostwald's school rejected them altogether—they were for the first time lifted to physical reality in the theory of gases by Maxwell and Boltzmann. In a gas, these particles are widely separated and engaged in violent motion; again and again they collide, rebound, etc. Following these processes in detail in thought led, for one thing, to full comprehension of *all* the properties of gases: their elastic and thermic properties, their viscosity, heat conductivity, and diffusion; and at the same time it led to a firm foundation of the mechanical theory of heat, namely, the theory that heat is the motion of these ultimate particles, which becomes increasingly violent with rising temperature. If this is true, then, through collisions with the surrounding molecules, small bodies— barely visible under the microscope—must be in continuous motion, which will increase with temperature. This motion of small suspended particles had already been discovered in 1827 by Robert Brown (a physician in London), but only in 1905 did Einstein and Smoluchoski demonstrate that it quantitatively corresponds to the theoretical expectations.

So much that is closely connected with our subject falls into this fertile period—about ten years before and after the turn of the century—that it becomes difficult to keep it all simultaneously in sight. There was the discovery of the X-rays—'light' of very short wave length; and of the cathode rays—streams of negatively charged corpuscles, the electrons. There were the radioactive decay and the radiation emitted in the process, partly streams of corpuscles, just those by whose spontaneous expulsion from the atomic nucleus one atom is transformed into another; partly 'light' of much shorter wave length which is formed at the same time. All the corpuscles carry electric charges; the charge is always the very small electric unit charge which Millikan has measured directly, or its exact double or triple. Also the masses of these particles could be very precisely measured, as could those of the atoms themselves. The determination of atomic masses, the so-called mass spectrography, was developed by Aston in Cambridge to such fabulous precision that he could establish beyond any doubt the negative answer to an age-old question: atomic masses are *not* integer multiples of a smallest unit. Nevertheless, we may conceive of them, or rather, of the heavy, but very small, positively charged atomic *nuclei*—the surrounding negative electrons weigh hardly anything—as made up of a number of hydrogen nuclei (protons) about half of which, though, have lost their positive unit charge (neutrons). Thus, e.g., in a normal carbon nucleus 6 protons and 6 neutrons are combined. It weighs, in units convenient for purposes of comparison:

| carbon nucleus | ........ | 12·00053 |
| compared to | $\begin{cases} \text{proton} \\ \text{neutron} \end{cases}$ | ........ 1·00758 <br> ........ 1·00898 |

The unit is $(1·6603) \, 10^{-24}$g, but does not interest us right now. How can the *mass defect* be explained, which, in our example, amounts already to almost a tenth of a unit? By the binding energy which is freed through the combination of these 12 particles and which is enormously greater in such 'nuclear reactions' than in the chemical reactions known from of old. In other words, the system loses potential energy while the 12 particles yield to the attractive forces by which they are then firmly held together. As mentioned above, this energy loss means according to Einstein a loss in mass. This is called the packing effect. The forces are of course not electrical forces— those are repellent—but the so-called nuclear forces, which are much stronger but act only within a very small range (about $10^{-13}$ cm.).

### 3. *Wave field and particle; their experimental detection*

Here you catch me already in a contradiction. Didn't I say at the beginning that we no longer assume the existence of forces and fields of force, in addition to matter and apart from it? I could easily talk myself out of it by saying: well, the force field of a particle is simply considered a part of it. But this is not the case. The well established view to-day is rather that everything—*anything at all*—is at the same time particle and field. Everything has the continuous structure with which we are familiar from the field, as well as the discrete structure with which we are equally familiar from particles. Expressed in such a general way this proposition has certainly a high degree of truth. For it is supported by innumerable experimental facts. In details, opinions differ, of which we shall speak later. Incidentally, in the particular case of the field of nuclear forces its particle structure is more or less known. Most likely the so-called *pi-mesons* are the corresponding particles; they appear among others in the splitting of an atomic nucleus and leave clear single tracks in a photographic emulsion. The nuclear particles themselves, on the other hand, the nucleons—as protons and neutrons are called by a common name—which everybody has always been accustomed to considering as discrete particles, when directed in swarms at a crystal surface, yield interference patterns which leave no doubt as to their continuous wave structure. The difficulty, in all cases equally great, of combining these two so very different character traits in *one* mental picture is still the main stumbling-block which causes our conception of matter to be so wavering and uncertain.

For neither the particle concept nor the wave concept is hypothetical. I mentioned in passing the tracks in a photographic emulsion each of which indicates the trajectory of a single particle. The tracks in the so-called cloud-chamber of C. T. R. Wilson have been known even longer. By means of these tracks extremely diverse and interesting details in the behaviour of single particles can be observed and measured: the bending of their paths (due to their electric charge) in a magnetic field; the mechanical laws governing the collisions which occur roughly as between ideal billiard balls; the disintegration of a heavy atomic nucleus through a 'direct hit' by one of those 'cosmic' particles coming out of the universe, rare in number, but possessed of incredibly high momentum, often several million times larger than elsewhere observed or artificially produced. This artificial production is being attempted right now at terrific expenditure, defrayed in the main by the various state ministries of defence. It is true that one cannot kill anybody with one such racing particle, or else we should all be dead by now. But their study promises, indirectly, a hastened realization of the plan for the annihilation of mankind which is so close to all our hearts.

It may be appropriate to mention that these interesting observations on single particles, which I cannot possibly exhaust in my short resumé, succeed only with very fast particles. Incidentally, the method of tracks is not the only one. The oldest you can easily try out yourself if some night after adaptation to the dark you look with a magnifying glass at a luminous numeral of your wrist-watch. You will find that it is not uniformly bright, but surges and undulates, just as a lake sometimes twinkles in the sun. Each scintillating sparklet is produced by a so-called alpha-particle (helium nucleus) expelled by a radioactive atom, which in this process is transformed into a different atom. And this goes on and on for many years —in a good Swiss watch. Another device that is used a great deal in studying cosmic rays is the Geiger-Müller counter which 'responds' when it is hit by a single effective particle. It is extremely valuable. For this 'response' can to-day easily be amplified to such an extent that it 'triggers' the expansion mechanism of a cloud-chamber and the shutter of a photographic camera directed onto it just when something interesting is going to happen in the chamber. This is one, though not the only, important use of these counters, half a hundred of which and more are often built in a complex array into a single apparatus.

So much for the observation of single particles. Now to the continuous field or wave character. The wave structure of visible light is rather coarse (its wave length is, roughly, about a two thousandth of a millimeter); it has been very intensively studied for more than a century by means of the phenomena which occur when two, or several, or very many, wave trains cross each other—the diffraction and interference phenomena. The principal means for the analysis and measurement of light waves is the ruled grating, which consists of a great many fine parallel equidistant lines, closely engraved on a specular metallic surface on which light impinging from *one* direction is scattered and collected in different directions depending on its wave length. For the very much shorter waves of the X-ray spectrum, as well as for the 'matter waves'—as which the particle streams of high velocity manifest themselves—even the finest ruled gratings which we can produce are somewhat too coarse. In 1912, Max von Laue discovered the instrument that since then has made possible the precise analysis of all these waves; he discovered it in the naturally grown crystal. His discovery was invaluable, unique in its way. Not only does it reveal the structure of the crystal—a highly regular arrangement of atoms in each of three directions: 'length', 'width', and 'height', repeating the same grouping innumerable times at constant intervals—but this discovery was *one* with the use of the periodic fine structure of crystals—instead of the ruled grating—for the analysis of waves. Please take note: the natural structure of crystals comes to our assistance just where it itself, i.e. the granular structure of matter, sets a limit to all precision mechanics. Gratings of such fineness could not be ruled because the 'material' is too coarse. With these crystal gratings first the wave nature of X-rays was ascertained and their wave lengths were measured, and later the same was done for matter waves, in particular for electron beams, but also for beams of other particles, such as neutrons and protons.

## 4. *Quantum theory: Planck, Bohr, de Broglie*

So far I have told you all sorts of things about the structure of matter, but we still have not mentioned Max Planck and his quantum theory. Everything I have reported so far might just as well have happened without it. How was it then? What about this quantum theory? Again, I shall not report the exact historical sequence, but rather how the situation appears to us to-day.

Planck told us in 1900—and the essential features are still true to-day—that he could comprehend the radiation of red-hot iron, or of an incandescent star such as the sun, only if this radiation is exclusively produced in portions and transferred in portions from one carrier to another (e.g. from atom to atom). This was startling, since this radiation concerns energy, originally an extremely abstract concept, namely, a measure of the interaction and effectiveness of those ultimate carriers. The division into circumscribed portions was extremely bewildering—bewildering not only to us, but also to Planck. Five years later, Einstein told us that energy has mass and mass is energy, in other words, that they are one and the same—and that,

too, is still true to-day. There, now, the scales are falling
from our eyes: our dear old atoms, corpuscles, particles,
are Planck's energy quanta. *The carriers of those quanta
are themselves quanta.* One gets dizzy. He notices that
something quite fundamental lies at the bottom which is
not yet understood. After all, the above-mentioned scales
did not fall suddenly. It took twenty or thirty years. And,
maybe, they still have not fallen completely.

The immediately following step was not quite so far-
reaching, but still important enough. Niels Bohr taught us
in 1913, by an ingenious and consistent generalization of
Planck's hypothesis, to understand the *line spectra* of
atoms and molecules, and at the same time the composition of these particles, from heavy, positively charged
nuclei and light electrons revolving around them, each of
which carries a negative unit charge. I cannot pause here
to explain the details of this important intermediate stage
of our knowledge. The basic idea is that each of these
small systems—atom or molecule—can only harbour definite
*discrete* energy quantities corresponding to its nature or
its constitution; and that, in transition from a higher to a
lower 'energy level', it emits the balance as a radiation
quantum of quite definite wave length *inversely proportional* to the quantum given off (which was already contained in Planck's original hypothesis).

This means that a quantum of given magnitude manifests itself in a periodic process of definite *frequency*
which is *directly proportional* to the quantum (the frequency equals the energy quantum divided by the famous
Planck's constant, h). It was not until 1925 that L. de
Broglie drew the inference which rather suggests itself
that a wave process of frequency $\dfrac{mc^2}{h}$ might be associated
with a particle mass m, which according to Einstein has
the energy $mc^2$ (c = velocity of light); this he did, first,
only for the mass m of the electron. A few years after this
famous dissertation of de Broglie's the 'electron waves'
required by his theory were demonstrated by experiment
in the way I have discussed above. This was the starting
point for the cognition which soon took root (we have

mentioned it before) that everything—*anything at all*—is
both particle and wave field. For after all, whenever we
hear from now on of a particle of mass m, we shall associate with it a wave field of the frequency $\frac{mc^2}{h}$. And
wherever we encounter a wave field of frequency v we
shall associate with it energy quanta hv or, what amounts
to the same, mass quanta $\frac{hv}{c^2}$. Thus de Broglie's dissertation was the starting point for the utter uncertainty of our
conception of matter. The particle picture as well as the
wave picture have truth value which we must not give up.
But we do not know how to combine them.

## 5.  *Wave field and particle: their theoretical connexion*

Yet, the *connexion* of the two pictures is known in full
generality with great precision and down to amazing details. Nobody doubts its correctness and universal validity.
But concerning the unification to a single, concrete, palpable picture opinions are so strongly divided that a great
many deem it altogether impossible. I shall now briefly
sketch the *connexion*. But do not expect that a uniform
concrete picture will emerge before you; and do not blame
the lack of success either on my ineptness in exposition
or your own denseness—nobody has as yet succeeded.

One distinguishes two things in a wave: *first of all* the
wave fronts which form a system of surfaces, like the
layers of an onion except for the fact that they *propagate*
perpendicular to the layers (i.e. perpendicular to themselves); you are familiar with the analogue in two (instead
of three) dimensions from the beautiful wave circles
which form on the smooth surface of a pond when a stone
is thrown in. The *second* characteristic, less intuitive, are
those imagined lines perpendicular to the wave fronts
along which, at each point, the wave travels: the *wave
normals*, which we also call *rays*, transferring an expression familiar to us from *light* to any kind of waves.

Here I falter. For what I am now going to say and

must say is important and fundamental, is even correct, yet it is only correct in such a severely restricted sense that it almost contradicts the provisional assertion. The provisional assertion is this: *These wave normals, or rays, correspond to the particle trajectories.* Indeed, if you cut a small piece out of a wave, approximately 10 or 20 wave lengths along the direction of propagation, and about as much across, and destroy the rest of the wave ('flatten' it), then such a 'wave packet' actually moves along a ray and with exactly the same velocity and possibly change of velocity as we might expect from a particle of this particular kind at this particular place, taking into account any force fields acting on the particle.

Although we obtain in the wave packet or wave group a more or less intuitive picture for the particle, which can be worked out in detail (e.g. the *momentum* of a particle increases as the wave length decreases: the two are inversely proportional), yet for many reasons we cannot take this intuitive picture quite seriously. For one thing, it is, after all, somewhat vague, the more so the greater the wave length; for another, quite often we are not dealing with a small packet but an extended wave; lastly, very small 'packetlets' may occur of a structure such that there can be no question of wave fronts and wave normals, an important case to which I shall come back in a moment. The following interpretation I consider appropriate and justifiable because it is extensively supported by experiments: at each position of a uniformly propagating wave train there is found a *twofold structural connexion of interactions* which may be distinguished as 'longitudinal' and 'transversal'. The transversal structure is that of the wave fronts and manifests itself in diffraction and interference experiments; the longitudinal structure is that of the wave normals and manifests itself in the observation of single particles. Both are fully established through ingenious experimental arrangements carefully thought out with a view to the particular purpose.

However, these concepts of longitudinal and transversal structures are not sharply defined and absolute, since the concepts of wave front and wave normal are not either.

They are necessarily lost if the whole wave phenomenon is reduced to a small region of the dimensions of a single or very few wave lengths. This case is of special interest, in particular for the waves which according to deBroglie represent the 'second nature' of the electron. For them it occurs just in the vicinity of a positively charged atomic nucleus, where the wave phenomenon, a kind of standing wave, is reduced to a small region whose calculated dimensions coincide very well with the true atomic size, which from other sources has been quite well known for a long time. You can produce standing water waves of a similar nature in a small basin if you dabble with your finger rather uniformly in its center, or else just give it a little push so that the water surface undulates. Here we are not dealing any more with uniform wave propagation; what catches the interest are the normal frequencies of these standing waves, which you can also quite well observe in the basin. The normal frequencies of the wave group washing around the atomic nucleus can be computed, and they are universally found to be exactly equal to the 'energy levels' of the aforementioned theory of Bohr's divided by Planck's constant, h. The ingenious, yet somewhat artificial, assumptions of that theory, as well as of the older quantum theory in general, are thus superseded by the far more natural idea of de Broglie's wave phenomenon. The wave phenomenon forms the 'body' proper of the atom. It takes the place of the individual pointlike electrons which in Bohr's model are supposed to swarm around the nucleus. Such pointlike single particles are completely out of the question within the atom, and if one still thinks of the nucleus itself in this way one does so quite consciously for reasons of expediency.

In the discovery that 'energy levels' are virtually nothing but the frequencies of normal modes of vibration, it seems to me particularly important that now one can do without the assumption of *sudden transitions,* since two or more normal modes may very well be simultaneously excited. The discreteness of the *normal frequencies* fully suffices—at least so I believe—to support the considerations from which Planck had started and many similar and just as important ones—I mean, in short, to support all of quantum thermodynamics.

## 6. *Quantum jumps and particle identity*

Abandoning the *theory of quantum jumps,* which to me personally are becoming more and more inacceptable as the years go on, has however far-reaching consequences. It means actually that one does not take seriously the exchange of energy in well-defined portions, does not really believe in it, but replaces it by resonance between vibrational frequencies. Yet, we have seen that, because of the identity of mass and energy, we must consider the corpuscles themselves as Planck's energy quanta. This is at first frightening. For the said disbelief implies that neither must we consider the individual particle as a well-defined permanent entity.

That it is, in fact, no such thing can also be reasoned in other ways. For one thing, for a long time properties have been attributed to such a particle that are in contradiction with such an assumption. From the picture of the 'wave packet', only passingly mentioned above, the famous uncertainty relation of Heisenberg's can easily be inferred, according to which a particle cannot simultaneously have a well-defined position and a sharply defined velocity. Even if this uncertainty were small—and this it is not—it implies that one can never be apodictically certain to observe the same particle twice. Another reason for not attributing identifiable sameness to the individual particle is the following: If in a theoretical consideration we are dealing with two or more particles of the same kind, e.g., with the two electrons of a helium atom, we must *obliterate their individualities,* or else the results will simply be false, will not agree with experience. Two situations that are only distinguished by the interchange of the two electrons must be counted not only as equal—this would be obvious—but as one and the same; if they are counted as *two* equal situations, nonsense obtains. This circumstance weighs heavily, because it holds for any kind of particle in arbitrary numbers without exception, and because it runs counter to everything that the old atomic theory had assumed about it.

Most theoreticians will probably admit that the individual particle is not a well-defined permanent entity of detectable identity or sameness and will accept the aforementioned reasons for the utter inadmissibility of such a view. Nevertheless, in their ideas, considerations, discussions, and papers, the individual particle still plays a rôle with which I cannot agree. Even deeper rooted is the picture of the sudden transitions, the 'quantum jumps', at least according to the words and phrases that have become common language; in a highly abstruse terminology, to be sure, whose common-sense meaning is often difficult to grasp. Thus the transition *probability* is part of the standing vocabulary. But, after all, one can speak of the probability of an event only if one believes that, occasionally, it actually occurs. And in that case, since *intermediate stages* are disclaimed, the transition must, indeed, be sudden. Moreover, if it took time, it might conceivably be interrupted halfway by an unforeseen disturbance; then one would be completely at sea, the allegedly precise and fundamental conceptual structure would be undermined. In these concepts probability generally plays a dominating role. The deeply felt dilemma *wave vs. corpuscle* is supposed to be resolved by asserting that the wave field merely serves for the computation of the *probability* of finding a corpuscle of given properties at a given position if one looks for it there. This interpretation may be quite appropriate to results obtained by special, ingeniously devised experimental arrangements with ultra-high-frequency waves ('ultrafast corpuscle streams'). I mean those results which I mentioned earlier as observations on single particles. In the tracks, called particle trajectories, a *longitudinal* interconnexion along the wave normal doubtlessly manifests itself. But such a connexion is definitely to be expected when a wave front is propagating. The chances of understanding it from the wave picture are certainly greater than, conversely, the chances of understanding the *transversal* interconnexion of interference and diffraction from the combined action of discrete single particles, once one deprives the waves of reality and grants them merely a kind of *informative* rôle.

## 7. *Identity of waves*

'Real existence' is, indeed, an expression which has been virtually chased to death by many philosophical hounds. Its simple, naïve meaning has almost become lost to us. Therefore I want to recall here something else. We spoke of a corpuscle's not being an individual. Properly speaking, one never observes the *same* particle a second time— very much as Heraclitus says of the river. You cannot mark an electron, you cannot 'paint it red'. Indeed, you must not even *think* of it as marked, or else you obtain, through false 'counting', wrong results at every step—for the structure of line spectra, in thermodynamics, and elsewhere. In contrast, it is, however, quite easy to imprint on a wave an individual structure by which it can be recognized beyond any doubt. Just think of the beacon-fires on sea. According to a definite code the light sequence of each is prescribed e.g., 3 seconds light, 5 seconds dark, 1 second light, another pause of 5 seconds, and again light for 3 seconds, etc. The skipper knows: That is San Sebastian. Something similar holds for whistle buoys, except here it is sound waves. Or, you talk across the Atlantic by wireless telephone with a close friend in New York; as soon as he says: 'Hello there, Eduard Meier speaking', you know that his voice has imprinted on the radio wave a structure which has travelled to you across five thousand miles and can beyond any doubt be distinguished from any other. But one does not even have to go that far. If your wife calls 'Francis' from the garden, it is exactly the same thing, except that the structure is imprinted on sound waves, the trip is shorter, but lasts longer. All our verbal communication is based on imprinted individual wave structures. And, according to the same principle, what a wealth of details is transmitted to us in rapid succession by the cinematographic or the television picture!

These, to be sure, are relatively coarse wave structures,

which perhaps should not be juxtaposed to individual
corpuscles, but to the palpable objects of our surroundings. And almost all of these have a very pronounced
individuality; my old pocket-knife, my old felt hat, the
Zürich Münster, etc., I have recognized a hundred times
beyond any doubt. But this characteristic—that individuality has to be ascribed to the wave phenomenon, in
contrast to corpuscles—is already found to a remarkable
extent in elementary waves. *One* example must suffice.
A limited volume of, say, helium gas can either be thought
of as consisting of many helium atoms, or, *instead*, it can
be looked upon as a superposition of elementary wave
trains of matter waves. Both views lead to the same
results as to the behaviour of the gas upon heating, compression, etc. But certain somewhat involved *enumerations*
to be applied in both cases have to be carried out in
different ways. If the mental picture used is that of the
particles, the helium atoms, then no individuality must be
ascribed to them, as I have said before. This appeared at
first very surprising and led to lengthy controversies, by
now, however, long settled. In the second view, however,
which concentrates on the matter wave trains *instead of*
on the particles, every one of the wave trains has a well-
defined structure which is different from that of any other.
It is true, there are many pairs of waves which are so
similar to each other that they could change roles without
any noticeable effect on the gas. But should one *count*
the *very many* similar states formed in this way as merely
a single one, the result would be quite wrong.

## 8. *Conclusion*

You may be surprised that in spite of everything that I
have put forward in the last part, and which nobody
actually denies, the closely connected concepts of *quantum
jump* and *individual corpuscle* have not yet disappeared
from the vocabulary, or the mental picture, of the physicist. You will find the explanation if you consider that the
view we have finally reached, and for which we have been
headed for the last third of this lecture, sets aside many

details about the structure of matter which I presented in the first two thirds, or at least casts doubts on their real meaning. But I could not—without insufferable long-windedness I just *could* not but use a language which I do not really consider appropriate. How can one ever determine the weight of a carbon nucleus and of a hydrogen nucleus, each to the precision of several decimals, and detect that the former is somewhat lighter than the twelve hydrogen nuclei combined in it, without accepting for the time being the view that these particles are something quite concrete and real? This view is so much more convenient and intuitive that we cannot do without it, just as the chemist does not discard his valence-bond formulas, fully realizing that they represent a drastic simplification of a rather involved wave mechanical situation.

If you finally ask me: Well, what *are* these corpuscles really, these atoms and molecules?—I must confess honestly I know the answer just as little as I know where Sancho Panza's second donkey came from. To say something at all, though nothing momentous: at the most, it may be permissible to think of them as more or less temporary entities within the wave field, whose form [Gestalt], though, and structural manifold in the widest sense, ever repeating themselves in the same manner, are so clearly and sharply determined by the wave laws that many processes take place *as if* those temporary entities were substantial permanent beings. Mass and charge of the particles, defined with such precision, must then be counted among the *structural* elements determined by the wave laws. *Conservation* of charge and mass in the large would have to be considered as a statistical effect, based on the 'law of large numbers'.

# On the Peculiarity
# of the Scientific World-View

## I. WHAT DISTINGUISHES OUR WAY OF THINKING?

### 1. *Where it stems from*

Out of my occasional studies of the philosophy of the Greeks there has come increasingly before me a question, the attempt to answer which, I find, throws a new light on certain perennial problems even though it may not solve them. How the question arises is best illustrated by quoting two distinguished scholars of classical antiquity.

In the preface to the fourth edition of his *Early Greek Philosophy* (London, A. & C. Black, 1930), John Burnet says: '. . . it is an adequate description of science to say that it is "thinking about the world in the Greek way." That is why science has never existed except among peoples who came under the influence of Greece.'

In the first volume of his masterwork *Griechische Denker* (3rd ed., p. 419) Theodor Gomperz speaks of the intellectual advantage that may be drawn from studying those ancient doctrines, notwithstanding the progress of the sciences in two and a half millennia. He points to the fact that during all this time several basic problems in science 'have often changed their appearance, but in essence have remained unaltered', and, indeed, still await their solution. He then continues:

It is of even greater importance to recall an *indirect* kind of application or utilization that . . . must be regarded as highly momentous. Nearly our entire intellectual education originates from the Greeks. A thorough knowledge of these origins is the indispensable prerequisite for *freeing* ourselves from their overwhelming influence. To ignore the past is here not merely undesirable, but simply impossible. . . . Our entire thinking, the logical categories in which it moves, the linguistic patterns it uses (being therefore dominated by them)—all this is in no small degree an artifact and is, in the main, the product of the great thinkers of antiquity. We must, indeed, investigate this process of becoming in all thoroughness, lest we mistake for primitive what is the result of growth and development, and for natural what is actually artificial.

It is not without interest to compare with this the views of Ernst Mach, to whom, too, the ideational history of our modern scientific world-view meant so much. Among his *Popular Lectures* (3rd ed., J. A. Barth, 1903) there is one (No. XVII) in which he, as one will at times, gives vent to his anger with the deficiencies of high-school instruction in classical philology, and with a sweeping stroke throws away the baby with the bath. He speaks rather disdainfully of the 'sparse and paltry remnants of ancient science' and finally sums up thus (p. 315 f.):

For our culture has gradually acquired full independence, soaring far above that of antiquity. It is following an entirely *new* trend. It centers around mathematical and scientific enlightenment. The traces of ancient ideas, still lingering in philosophy, jurisprudence, art and science, constitute impediments rather than assets, and will come to be untenable in the long run in face of the development of our own views.

## 2. *Comparison of these judgments*

Burnet, Gomperz, and Mach all agree on this, that our age is dominated by the spirit of natural science. But whereas the two classical scholars make the powerful, even over-powering, influence of *our* antiquity responsible, the physicist sees in it the overcoming of antiquity. The contrast may be less blatant than it seems at first glance. What our admirable expert of the modern history of science—since the Renaissance—neglects, is the objects of comparison which are far removed. Resemblance between members of a family escapes us easily if we are in daily contact with them and know them intimately. To the extent that our knowledge of other cultures progresses, of older ones which preceded ours, and of others which arose in parallel but almost entirely separately in the Far East, the distance in time and ideas between an Ernst Mach and a Thales of Miletus diminishes, and the spiritual family relationship of grandson to ancestor is more apparent to us than to him.

One should also recall the following: Practically every line of Plato's has come down to us in a careful, hardly spoiled text, and so has after all the larger and more important part of Aristotle's surprisingly extensive works; but only a small fraction of the writings of the Pythagoreans, the Ionian philosophers of enlightenment, and the atomists have been preserved, mostly sparse fragments which are interspersed as quotations in the reports of others about the life and teachings of these men.[1] The painstaking sifting and collecting of these fragments by Ritter and Preller, Diels, Usener, et al. took place during Mach's lifetime. The discrepancy in the preservation is doubtless partly due to the preference for Plato and Aristotle and the high regard for them on the part of Christian theology. Actually they were, indeed, close to Christianity owing to their high ethical ideals, their emphatic affirmation of the immortality of the soul—while maintaining a quite reserved attitude with respect to the Pythagorean teachings of metempsychosis. They were

[1] An exception is the extensive compendium of Hippocratic writings and three letters of Epicurus's in Laertius Diogenes in which E. himself gives a short outline of his philosophy. S. Cyril Bailey, *Epicurus, The Extant Remains*, Oxford 1926 (original text, English translation and commentary).

practically 'nostrified' by Christianity and had, as is well-known, a lasting influence on it. So much more weighty was, therefore, the accusation of atheism levelled against the Ionian enlightenment already by Plato, an accusation which soon was extended to atomism. To ward it off from the latter, Epicurus's and Lucretius's truly fanatical fight against the idea of immortality was as little suited as their naïve adherence to the anthropomorphic gods of Graeco-Roman mythology.

However this may be, even an unbiased philologist can only deal with what he has, not with what has been lost. Thus it was already due to the overwhelming volume of the material saved through the centuries that for a long time, and even to-day, whenever Greek philosophy is mentioned, the names and systems of Plato and Aristotle and their disciples and later successors flash up, and nothing else. Mach's above-quoted words mainly refer to them, as becomes quite evident from subsequent parts of the essay from which they are taken. His sharply derogatory judgment is to be understood as a reaction against a widespread overestimation.[2] One might wonder why the early atomists were not closer to the physicist—if one did not know that Mach was also strongly opposed to the modern atomic theory. And if he ever opened *De rerum natura* by Lucretius Carus in order to inform himself of the opinion of the ancients on this point, the work of this great poet, but with regard to contemporary (!) science a completely uninformed dilettante, was hardly suited to make out a convincing case.

## 3. *Formulation of the question*

If we take the above-mentioned statements of Burnet and Gomperz together, we come to the conclusion that the

---

[2] *Benjamin Farrington* [*Greek Science, its meaning for us (Thales to Aristotle)*. Pelican Books A 142] has given a valuable reappraisal of the subject. But already the above-mentioned works of Burnet and Gomperz impressively demonstrate the significance of the Ionian natural philosophers as the founders of natural science.

scientific world-view is a particular mental attitude discovered by Greek thinkers and descended from them to us. Let us assume this as our *working hypothesis*. Its validity can only be examined by trying to find a reasonable answer to the following question which grows out of it naturally: what are the characteristic features that distinguish this scientific-Greek way of thinking and differentiate it from others which are not necessarily to be preferred, yet worthy of attention? I am quite aware that I am only insufficiently equipped to answer such a comprehensive question. I shall be well satisfied if my imperfect attempt at a solution stimulates others to think about this matter. For the present, it seems to me—as I indicated at the outset—that certain inadequacies of the scientific world-view which have troubled men's minds time and again can be, if not removed, at least shown to be natural consequences of the original particular standpoint.

## 4. *Sketch of the answer*

This particular standpoint seems to me to embody two basic attitudes:

  (a) the assumption that the course of natural events can be understood (hypothesis of comprehensibility);

  (b) exclusion of or dispensing with the cognizing subject (from the understandable world-picture aspired to), who steps back into the rôle of an external observer (objectivation).

(a) *The hypothesis of comprehensibility.* This may at first seem utterly trivial. No wonder—all our thinking is tied up in it; the matter appears to us self-evident. But it does not come first. First comes animism. Obviously we shall not go very deeply into that but, so to speak conversely, we shall deal with Mach's positivism, which developed in the fight against animism in order to eliminate metaphysics from physics. It seems to us that he is overshooting his mark, and we shall try to show in Section II that *the hope that nature can be understood* does extend somewhat further than to a complete, most simple, and thought-economic description of experience.[3] And that it may extend further without yet relapsing into animism. The fact alone that economy and a successful mental supplementation of experience, in particular extrapolation to the future, are at all possible, presupposes a definite quality of experience: *it can be ordered.* This is a fact that itself demands an explanation. And it is not a pseudo-problem. It is true that our ordered thinking could only develop on the basis of this feature. Nevertheless, we can in our imagination compare it with its opposite, we can fancy ourselves with our ordered thinking being suddenly transported into a topsy-turvy world. Furthermore, the explanation cannot be found in the cold facts themselves, not even in their being ordered—that would be circular reasoning—but only in certain special characteristics which this order displays. And, indeed, the mechanical theory of heat and Darwinism have already had great successes in this direction.

In Section III the hypothesis of comprehensibility will be briefly compared with others, and gaps will be demonstrated that are left in the world-picture, due to the restriction it imposes—for it *does* impose restrictions.

(b) *Objectivation.* By this we mean what is also called the hypothesis of a real world around us. It is not trivial that we are dealing here, as I maintain, with an at first unconscious and incomplete simplification of the problem of nature by preliminary exclusion of the cogniz-ing subject from the complex of what is to be understood. The fact that objectivation amounts to the retreat of one's own person into the rôle of an onlooker who himself does not belong in the picture, is veiled by the following two consecutive circumstances. First of all, my body, to which my mental life proves to be so directly attached, is part of the object, the real external world which I construct.

[3] For quite a while I was undecided whether or not to reverse the order of discussion of (a) and (b). Whoever is bored with the discussion of positivism may omit reading Section II or turn immediately to Section IV, where he will find what I care most about.

Secondly, the same holds true for the bodies of other people. If it appears natural to include one's own sphere of consciousness in the real world, this holds even more so for the *spheres of consciousness* attached to other bodies, those usually being hypostatized as essentially different from one's own consciousness. This inclusion is based on the circumstance that those foreign spheres of consciousness are sufficiently attested to as to exclude for me any doubt in their reality; on the other hand, they are to me personally completely and utterly inaccessible. Hence, one concludes, they must be objective, i.e., one includes them in the object, the real world. Since, one argues further, they are different from one another and from one's own not in kind, but only in individuality, anything that holds for them must also hold for one's own consciousness.

It is this chain of false conclusions from which the main antinomies arise, the amazement that the objective world-picture is 'colorless, cold, and silent', the vain search for the point where 'spirit moves matter', etc. A discussion of these ideas will be found in Section IV. But it ought to be said that the two points that we are taking up in succession, the hypothesis of comprehensibility and objectivation, cannot really be separated but form a whole. The cut is artificial, the division serves only the purpose of analysis. In short: comprehensibility is bought at the price of letting the subject recede, which makes objectivation possible. And thus, as we have said above, it remains for the reader to decide whether or not he wants to read the following three sections in reversed order; this has for him the advantage of learning first what to us is most essential.

## II. THE ACHIEVEMENT OF THE
## COMPREHENSIBILITY HYPOTHESIS

### 5. *Historical notes*

The hypothesis of comprehensibility goes back to the Ionian natural philosophers of the 6th century B.C., among whom I also like to include—apart from Thales, Anaximander, and Anaximenes—Xenophanes and Heraclitus, while regarding Leucippus and Democritus certainly as their immediate spiritual heirs. This hypothesis is the truly great achievement of that movement. It has often been emphasized—the clear recognition probably goes back to F. Max Müller—that at the outset it was natural for man to trace back the grandiose events of nature, like wind and clouds, thunder and lightning, tempests at sea, earthquakes, roaring mountain torrents, the motions of heavenly bodies, and the growth of plants, to the only cause of remarkable events directly known to him, i.e., to the acts of volition of individuals. It was a step of great import to replace this etiology—at a time when it was not yet doubted by the multitude and when it determined to a large extent their practical behaviour—by the assumption that the world is an intelligible mechanism whose functioning can be explored by observation and reflexion and can even be predicted to one's own advantage.

The naïve pictures of the nature of things at which those pioneers of reason arrived are no longer of particular interest to us. Only sparse fragments of their presumably extensive writings are preserved in their own words, and in addition more or less lengthy reports, frequently from the pen of historiographers to whom the scientific problems meant much less than the composition of readable and stimulating life histories for the educated public. The true meaning of quite a few fragments separated from their context often remains doubtful and obscure, and the total world-picture which after a thorough study of all sources has been attributed to Thales or Heraclitus remains uncertain and rather indistinct. But it is not the particulars of the world-picture that constitute the significance of these men and this epoch for the history of ideas; it is, as we have said, rather the fact that the attempt had been made at all—and very likely for the first time in history—to understand Nature without any props, without mysticism or the intervention of superhuman personalities. For the first time the idea turns up that it should be possible to trace back the manifold of phenomena to **a** few simple fundamental principles—what later times called laws of Nature; the idea that in Nature everything comes to pass in a natural way; the hope that once the true principles have been found and the laws and regularities that follow from them clearly understood, the helpless amazement and fear in the face of Nature could be overcome, and the uncertainty of one's expectations would be greatly reduced. This was an immense anticipation. It *was* the basic idea of natural science.

Just as we have not gone into the untenable details, we shall not dwell here on the manner in which, through rigorous and logical steps starting from the concept of a uniform basic element (Thales, Anaximander) which *is conserved* even in gross-form changes of matter like melting and evaporation and, in particular, density changes (Anaximenes), the idea emerged that at the basis of *everything* are immutable, rigid ultimate particles distinguished only by their shapes, not by their substance, moving in empty space, acting on each other only by collisions, and producing all the phenomena we observe by their various shapes, configurations, and mutual impact-interactions. However, the declaration of war against superstition and the belief in the spirit world, and the honest desire to understand Nature, did not destroy the respect for her, but rather was consonant with emotions of deepest reverence for her godliness—as is evidenced by Xenophanes. Delightful is his mockery of the humans who believe that the gods are begotten and wear clothes as they do and who moreover impute to these sublime beings all that is held vile among mortals, such as lying, thievery, deceit, and adultery. If horses and cattle had hands and could paint with them—thus he scoffs—they would impart to their gods the shapes of horses and cattle; just as the

Ethiopians imagine their gods black and snub-nosed, the Thracians theirs blond and blue-eyed. But then, fragments like the following have been preserved from his poem:

(fr. 23) *One* god, the greatest among gods and men  
Neither in form like unto mortals nor in thought.

(fr. 24) He is all-seeing, he is all-thinking, he is all-hearing.

(fr. 25) But without any effort he swayeth all things by the thought of his mind.

Comprehensibility of the world became the basic tenet of atomism. In its last great representative in antiquity[4] we encounter it in the form that nothing but a fundamental understanding of Nature and of the natural causes acting in it can impart to the sage the imperturbability and peace of mind (*ataraxía*) which are indispensable to a happy life. It is true that perusing his didactic letters one cannot help noticing that he was already fairly removed from the spirit of the Ionians. One gains the impression that he and his disciples were mostly concerned with that *ataraxía*; it was not so much a genuine unquenchable thirst for a true knowledge of Nature that pervaded 'the garden'. All was well if for a heavenly phenomenon such as thunder and lightning or the annual course of the sun, three or four possible causes could be specified: one of them will be correct; which one, it is, of course, not possible to say, but that does not trouble one's peace of mind. Epicurus stands at the start of a decline of the natural sciences which was to last for many centuries.

## 6. *What does understanding mean?*

According to the views of modern philology,[5] it was Epicurus who had already made quite a sizeable breach in

---

[4] See the above-mentioned three didactic letters of Epicurus.  
[5] S. Cyril Bailey, op. cit., p. 186 (commentary to § 43 of the letter to Herodotus) and p. 339 (commentary to the letter to Menoeceus).

the hypothesis of comprehensibility, a breach which is remarkably similar to the psycho-physiological conclusions that in quite recent times some quantum theoreticians have been inclined to draw from Heisenberg's indeterminacy principle. The only evidence, however, is to be found in Lucretius's didactic poem,[6] and for me, at least, it is difficult to comprehend that Epicurus in his didactic letter to Herodotus—comprising about eighteen pages in modern type and expounding the basic precepts of his physics—should have mentioned this all-important doctrine of his system either not at all or only in four words (*hai dè katà parénklisin*), which have been inserted as a *conjecture* (out of fifteen words altogether) into a short gap in the text. I am referring to the following: Democritus had held onto strict determinism in the atom physics, even though he hardly failed to notice the well-known fatalistic difficulty to which this leads; in particular, since he (as also Epicurus and Lucretius) regarded the soul too as consisting of material atoms, albeit very tiny and mobile ones. From Lucretius we learn that the atoms do after all constantly depart from their mechanically predictable paths in *extremely* small perturbations indeterminate with respect to place and time (*parénklisis*), and only thus are the free voluntary movements of beast and man to be understood.

The changes of the concept of 'comprehensibility' extend throughout the European history of ideas during the subsequent two thousand years, most prominently at times when the science of Nature, 'physiology' in the sense of ancient Greek, becomes the focus of interest, as in the periods of the French and English Enlightenment. Since we neither can nor want to write here an outline of the history of philosophy, let us turn without delay to the more recent and still acute phase of the matter.

Hidden remnants of *animism* were even to be found in physics until quite recently. Even to-day, they have not vanished from the customary view of Nature. As Mach correctly points out, a trace of animism adheres even to the abstract idea that we characterize by the pair of

[6] *De rerum natura*, II, 216 ff.

concepts, cause and effect. David Hume's critique, exhaustive and conclusive as one may regard it, could not once and for all eliminate causality. It is too deeply rooted in the thinking of everyday life and in the language, too important a logogramm (in the sense of the stenographer). It is, however, surprising to encounter it in Kant's table of categories so shortly after Hume's funeral sermon. In physics, force as 'the cause of motion' is very much in the foreground. The concept is evidently abstracted from the volitional act of muscle innervation and the feeling of pressure accompanying it if, as a result, one of our limbs puts into motion or arrests another body. We may protest that we omit from the physical concept of force the characteristic of *intention* which is inseparably attached to the psycho-physiological model; still, it remains doubtful whether we have succeeded as long as we put the cause-and-effect relationship as proxy, as it were, in its place, the *causa efficiens* in place of the *causa finalis*. It still *effects* the result, even though it does so unconsciously, without *aiming* at it. It *is* somebody or something. A nobody or a nothing cannot even have an effect.

This is why Kirchhoff strongly advocated that in mechanics force must mean nothing but the product of mass and acceleration. Newton's law of motion, which states this equality, becomes thereby neither tautological nor trivial. On the contrary, its true content appears even clearer after being divested of dross: bodies determine one another's accelerations—and not velocities or anything else. (Aristotle believed that bodies have natural *places* to which they are attracted, the light ones upward, the heavy downward.) Kirchhoff specified as the task of mechanics to describe the motions occurring in Nature completely and in the simplest manner.

In a similar and even more general vein others before Kirchhoff had already expressed themselves.[7] Supported by the consent of the 'most exact' and 'most mathematical' field of the natural sciences, mechanics—where it struck one as the most paradoxical—the idea that all that is involved in natural science is the complete, most simple,

[7] E. Mach, op. cit., no. xv, p. 263.

thought-economic (Mach) description of the actual findings has attained tremendous significance. To many it
appears to-day as the alpha and omega of the philosophy
of physics. As is well-known, Ernst Mach became its
pioneer. He formulated the important principle of parsi-
mony or thought-economy; it means, on the one hand,
that for ever-increasing spheres of phenomena a *uniform*
description is obtained by the powerful means of mathematics, and on the other, that from the physical world-
picture all superfluous features are omitted, all those
which are not required by the observed facts—and hence
are not attested to. Entirely fascinated by the idea of
evolution, which in the Darwinian version started to
expand its immense force into all fields of human endeavour and thinking, Mach found for the progress of
scientific knowledge a very happy characterization: it
consists of a gradual, step-by-step adjustment of our ideas
to the facts. It is the aim and purpose of the adjustment,
according to him, to obtain the capacity of supplementing
in one's mind the given facts as completely as possible by
other facts not or not yet given. To supplement facts in
his mind, that was what the scientist was striving to
achieve.

## 7. *Prediction—touchstone or goal?*

This attitude of strict neutrality, purely observing and
registering, is called Machian positivism. It originated as
a wholesome reaction against verbal or specious explanations which easily obstruct further exploration of facts by
prematurely setting one's mind at rest; as, for example, if
the quite specific behaviour of living substance is attributed to a special life force acting within, instead of explor-
ing whether or not it differs from inorganic matter already
in its material (atomic) composition so strongly and in
just such a way as to lead us to expect also a fundamentally different behaviour.

   If, on the other hand, we are told—and we have been
told this—that explaining and understanding beyond pure
description do not have any tangible meaning, this again

seems to obstruct the path of progress in knowledge by preventing the discovery of genuine explanations. Positivism does not exhaust what we mean in this essay by the hypothesis of comprehensibility. That is the reason that we must come to terms with it here.

I know, its main thesis is difficult to attack. Its position is very strong. It certainly is the only touchstone for a physical theory in that it permits, within the domain of facts to which it refers, correct prediction from the exact data of an experimental arrangement the phenomena to be observed with it. But let us now assume that in some field, say, in electrodynamics, all interconnexions are satisfactorily known and precisely described; the field of these phenomena with all their interconnexions stands then before our mind's eye as a shape or form (*Gestalt*); a shape whose contours we assume to be fully ascertained and not subject to any change. But may it not possess inner configurational (*Gestalt*) relations which are interesting and significant, and should we not be permitted to search for them and to think about them? Is that supposed to be as meaningless as speculating about a cloud which now looks like a camel, now like a whale, and yet is neither?

'Not at all', the positivist will reply, 'by all means, do so. In particular, do search for configurational relations between different shapes of this kind, i.e., between theories that are fairly well-established in various parts of the field. This is precisely the way to a simpler, more comprehensive, more thought-economic description. But don't deceive yourself that in this way you will ever get beyond pure description. You cannot look behind the scenes.'

To this we should like to answer—and I believe many will join us—however this may be, what matters to us is essentially the *picture* which is eventually or at any given step obtained; we are interested in the shape itself of the interconnexions. Foretelling, predicting, observations is only a means for us to ascertain whether or not the picture that we have formed is correct.

'Very well,' says the positivist, 'there is not really so much difference between us; provided you remain honest

and understand by 'picture' or 'shape' only the total co-
ordination and organization of real or possible observa-
tional data without any basically unobservable embellish-
ments, products of your imagination, which you concoct
in order to *explain* the real world, as you call it. But I
know your kind. You are much rather inclined to regard
and to display, not the facts themselves, but precisely
those auxiliary structures as your 'findings', as the real
achievement. And there I refuse to go along. Whatever is
not directly related to possible sense perceptions must be
omitted.'

## 8. *Are unobservable traits admissible? The example of the historical sciences*

Let us take a closer look at this reproach. Mach has
emphasized that the desired supplementation in thought
does not always concern the future. He says:[8] 'One
demands of science that it know how to predict. . . . The
expression, though suggesting itself, is however too narrow. The geologist and the palaeontologist, occasionally
the astronomer, always the historian, sociologist, philologist, predict, as it were, backward. The descriptive
sciences, just like geometry, mathematics, predict neither
forward nor backward, but try to find the conditional for
the conditions. Let us say rather: science has to supplement in thought partially available facts.'

Occasional predictions of astronomy into the past may
refer to events like the famous solar eclipse in the year
585 B.C., the calculation of which from modern data
furnished an important clue for the biographers of Thales
of Miletus. But if we look to the sciences that regularly
'predict backward'—the historical sciences in a somewhat
wider sense—we are struck by the fact that they seem to
regard their reversed predictions as the real result of their
research. Under no circumstances would they be willing,
for thought-economic reasons, to exclude as dead weight

---

[8] *Populäre Schriften*, 3rd ed., Leipzig, J. A. Barth, 1903,
p. 280 f. in the lecture "Über das Prinzip der Vergleichung in
der Physik," Naturforscherversammlung, Vienna 1894.

the assertions about the past which were deduced, often in a very circuitous and ingenious manner, by comparative studies of petrefacts, or of old manuscripts, or of archaeological findings. And yet, these assertions cannot be tested by direct experience. In their totality they form a mental supplementation to the only data accessible to us, namely, the natural or artificial records, remnants, inscriptions, finds, traditions, etc. To co-ordinate these directly accessible data and to *understand* them is the purpose of this supplementation, which itself, by definition, does not contain anything that is observable. An understanding thus obtained may at times be tested for its accuracy in much the same way as in the physical sciences. As in these, it may lead to a correct prediction of something empirically accessible, e.g., in geology to the prediction of metallic deposits; the archaeologist may decipher inscriptions which point to an earlier settlement at a certain place and time; one searches for the ruins, finds them in the expected layer. Not always, of course. Some things have 'vanished from the face of the earth' without a trace. Nor, it is true, are the ruins ever identical with the flourishing populous center of commerce which has arisen before our mind's eye. This latter will remain, from the standpoint of science, an unverifiable mental construct created to establish a correlation between all the encountered records and remnants and to assign to them their proper place within the larger context of the history of civilization.

I should like to know how the historical sciences should set about even expressing these correlations in words, not to speak of using them as goal markers for the progress of their investigations, if they were to renounce such constructs which, on the contrary, they actually regard as the tangible result of their work, the *object* proper of their studies. This object, the vivid and colourful picture of past events, is one hundred percent purely ideal. It remains forever in our imagination, not the slightest bit of it can be transformed into actual sense perceptions. Should one, therefore, omit it and study only the actual remains; and express their correlations in cautious phrases in which the little words 'as if' would be repeated ad

nauseam? I should like to know who would regard that
as a thought-economic advantage.

## 9.  *Does physics need pictures?*

It is very strange which branches of knowledge are mentioned by Mach—and even more so which are not—as
instances where prediction is directed neither forward nor
backward but to simultaneous occurrences. With regard to
the 'descriptive' sciences, as they were called at the time,
one is apt to think of a boy who has identified a flower
and puts it into his herbarium, happily convinced that it
will certainly comply with the full description of the
species even in those criteria which have not been applied.
In addition, Mach only mentions mathematics (and geometry). Now mathematics is, in this connexion indeed,
highly problematic. Certainly, 'conditioned-ness' here is of
quite a different nature than in all other cases. Why, one
asks oneself, go to such lengths to find examples and omit
to mention physics and chemistry, which are so much
more to the point? We take readings on the manometer
of the pressure in a boiler and we can deduce from them
the temperature with the help of a vapour-pressure table.
We see that a particular line appears in a spectrum and
know that, now, there is lithium vapour in the flame, and
so on and so forth. In these and in many other more or
less trivial cases, the supplemented simultaneous characteristic could in principle be directly tested. But there is in
physics and chemistry also the less trivial case of mental
constructs which have two points in common with those
in history, archaeology, and so on. Firstly, they are almost
indispensable for an understanding of the observed relations between perceivable characteristics, yet, they themselves cannot be made accessible to the senses, or at least
not to the same extent as they must be imagined in order
to serve that purpose. Nevertheless—and this is the second
point—these constructs are regarded by those to whom
they are dear as the really valuable result of their work,
as the ideal image of their subject produced by their
efforts and as such, as it were, revered.

Mach's attitude toward such constructs was determined by his epistemological principle. He rejected them according to the exact measure of their surmised unobservability. I.e., the wave theory of light was, of course, accepted, but atomistic and molecular concepts were radically repudiated and their speedy decline predicted. To disparage him to-day would be a cheap triumph. But in view of the fundamental rôle which this enticing principle is still, or again, accorded by the Neo-Machians in present-day quantum mechanics, it seems to me right to recall emphatically his wrong prognosis and, in particular, the fact that it was a consequence of his exaggerated methodology. Has it been forgotten that, at a decisive turn, it has virtually failed completely, has led in a diametrically opposite direction? This alone should make it highly questionable, in keeping with Mach's own basic tenets according to which it is only the practical success of a theory that counts.

To-day we are told—and with express reference to Mach—that we must not expect more from our science than those ad nauseam reiterated prophecies. Away with 'image-worship'. Let us only have differential equations or other mathematical procedures and a recipe for deriving from them and from a set of actually performed observations all statements about all future observations of which foreknowledge is in principle at all possible. The desire to visualize, so we are told, means wanting to know how Nature is really constituted, and that is metaphysics—an expression that in present-day science is mainly used as an insult.

As is well known, Heisenberg's uncertainty assertion is strongly involved in the discussion. Crossed with Mach's principle it leads to the view that even straightforward observation of and experimentation with ordinary inanimate matter all at once confronts us with the whole profound perplexity of the subject-object relationship. If those who believe that were right, it would mean for us here that the intelligible objectified world-picture (i.e., formally freed of the subject), the possibility of which forms the subject of this study, fails already in a much more primi-

tive way than only in the points that will be treated in
the third and fourth sections and that are actually quite
irrelevant to the physicist and chemist in their laboratories; it would mean that even for them it fails and that
not only in some specific form under consideration, but
in any one at all that we might try to give it.

Perhaps this possibility cannot be ruled out. I do not
think it is likely. So far it seems to me that the only reason
for the iconoclastic uproar is the following: the corpuscle
concept has, it is true, become the unquestioned and inalienable possession of the physicist who continuously uses
it as a mental construct in his laboratory and at his desk,
but, on the other hand, it leads to considerable embarrassment because we have not yet succeeded in fusing it with
the wave concept which, as one knows to-day, ought to be
applied not to different phenomena, but rather to exactly
the same ones as the corpuscle concept, i.e., both have to
be applied to simply everything. Some people believe they
have in Mach's principle found a wonderful way out of
this dilemma which frees us from the obligation to search
for clear conceptions of Nature by condemning the belief
in them as gross superstition.

## 10. *The picture is not only a permissible tool, but also a goal*

But it is hard to understand why that which is self-evident
in the historical sciences ought to pass for heresy in the
physical sciences, namely, to deal with events and situations that are inaccessible to direct observation. The historical sciences do that almost exclusively. Everybody
must admit that in a certain sense it is also unavoidable
in physics. The inmost bowels of the earth, the interiors
of the sun and the stars, belong here; even that sun, moon,
and stars float as material bodies tangibly in space at
distances that cannot be verified by a surveyor's chain and
that they would resist an impinging meteorite, are unobservable traits of the world-picture which we neither
ought nor want to omit from it. Why should we be *com-
pelled* to deal differently with the interior of the atom?

Why should we here be allowed to take recourse to an epistemological principle as an excuse for our failures?

It seems to me that what we are striving for here (in physics) as well as there (in history) is a comprehensive picture of the subject under investigation, a picture which becomes ever more distinct, lucid, and clearly understood in its interrelations. Here, as there, the coherence would be utterly destroyed if we felt bound by pangs of conscience to omit all that is not directly ascertained or cannot, if so desired, be confirmed by sense perceptions; if we felt bound to formulate all propositions in such a way that their relations to sense perceptions were immediately manifest.

## 11. *Intelligible chance: the theory of heat*

In the introduction, Section 4(a), we have already remarked that even from a strictly Machian standpoint a scientific 'description' is not a mere chronicle of events; not a tale in which first this happened, then that happened; but an assertion that *whenever* this takes place, that happens afterwards. In short: we have before us a description of past experiences coupled with the assertion that they would, under suitable circumstances, repeat themselves in the same order and with the same interdependence. And this assertion is not empty. It is an essential part of the statement. Moreover, it is a regular, recurrent contribution which cannot be settled or replaced by a declaration that is to hold once and for all. For this 'whenever' does not hold for every sequence of events but only for some; there are others. The possibility of ordering the course of Nature into regular sequences of events for which 'whenever' is true, is in itself a feature for which one would like to understand the reason. Can one?

In a certain sense, yes. As was already shown by Franz Exner in his lectures (published in 1919 by Franz Deuticke, Vienna), the regularities which the mechanical theory of heat traces back to the statistics of extremely frequent single events are quite independent of whether the single events forming the material of the statistics are on their part strictly, 'causally', determined, as had been assumed up to that point, or whether they were perhaps originally chance events involving considerable scattering of the results even for identical initial conditions. Exner surmised the latter. It so happened that a few years later the same conjecture was launched on the part of quantum mechanics and soon was incorporated in its credo. Exner's name is never mentioned in this context, probably because he published his ideas not in a learned journal but in a readable text-book without pretentious mathematics.

However, the important point in his consideration is not what in the last resort is the truth about elementary processes, but the fact that it is of no import for the observed regularities. They are in any case only a consequence of the statistics of very large numbers. They are thus directly reduced to the simplest mathematical concept there is, to integers. The ordered sequence of events which we encounter is produced in a manner which appears to us natural and quite transparent; one might say: by intelligible chance.

Is this a theoretical explanation of the *law of induction?* That is quite a ticklish question. A posteriori, yes. A posteriori means: after we have built up a system of physics that finally leads to Boltzmann's theory of irreversibility and of the regularities in Nature. But obviously, we could never have built this edifice of ideas without constantly making use of induction for the generalization of observations. And induction is still suspended in mid air. It is a loan. It is paid back only in the end, after exposing in Boltzmann's theory the structure of macroscopic events, the structure on which the actual strength of induction is based; the structure of macroscopic events being always produced by the combined action of innumerable similar microscopic partial events. Is that now circular reasoning?

## 12.  Darwin's theory of evolution

However that may be, the mechanical theory of heat in the form that Boltzmann has given to it represents a positive success in explanation and does not only concern one aspect of the phenomena, as the name 'theory of heat' seems to imply, but is truly of all-embracing significance for our entire understanding of Nature. It simply bursts the framework of 'mere economic description'. Another success of at least as much import concerning a much more involved stage of interrelations in Nature is Darwin's theory of evolution. In their fundamental structure the two theories have a great deal in common. The statistical random selection from very large (though not quite *that* large) populations, occurring again and again and again, that is exactly the 'mechanism' which, according to Darwin, leads to the formation and propagation of viable species. Just as in the theory of heat, the principle of explanation is *intelligible chance;* it is understandable to us that a mutation, no matter how little it may favour its carrier, must eventually accumulate if out of a very numerous progeny only a small fraction of each generation is selected by chance for survival. It is not only understandable, it is self-evident, it is a matter of definition. For what else should 'favouring' mean, but to increase a little the chances for survival or the statistical fraction of survivors? The rest is simple mathematics. Again we are dealing with a reduction to the simple concept of integers, and this feature has acquired an even deeper significance than in the original Darwinian version since it has turned out that the continuous variations which Darwin had in mind are to be replaced by de Vries's discontinuous mutations because only these are hereditary, and not the former.

## 13. *More about induction*

The adaptation theory illuminates the genesis of the law of induction from an entirely different side. In a world that takes a course obedient to law for reasons that the mechanical theory of heat has explained, the following property will be favourable to a living being: the property to react again with the motor act, $M$, to the *repetition* of an environmental situation, $U$, in which the living being has already once or more often *asserted* himself by way of $M$.

We shall, therefore, not be surprised that such a property has selective value and evolves not only with respect to a single $U$, but to all relevant environmental situations. It is the typical and general form of adaptation to an environment behaving in a lawful manner in which the recurrent situation $U$ has also the same consequences in the face of which $M$ has already once proved itself.

So far, there has been no mention of an act of consciousness, and none need demonstrably be involved; the consideration may also be applied to plants. If, though, in a higher animal the reaction habit, as we may call it, $U \rightarrow M$, which has evolved, is of such a kind that it enters consciousness, it might there—more or less clearly— be reflected in the manner that $M$ is chosen because it had been successful with regard to the former consequences of $U$ which are expected to recur.

This seems to me to be the reason that the induction principle forces itself upon us with such inescapable urgency, without any reflexion and prior to all theory; it is the mental concomitant of the only practical behaviour by which we can assert ourselves in the face of a world that follows a lawful course.

You will not overlook the following: it is again the mechanical theory of heat that carries the burden of responsibility for the actually lawful behaviour.

# III.  THE GAPS THAT ARE LEFT BY THE HYPOTHESIS OF COMPREHENSIBILITY

## 14.  *Contrasting it with other ways of thinking*

A full impression of the peculiarity of the comprehensibility hypothesis can really be obtained only by vividly imagining oneself in a mental situation to which it is foreign. This is not at all simple in our environment. Even superstition, belief in ghosts, spiritism, astrology, etc., though they are still fairly wide-spread, are comparatively mild phenomena, which have been tamed by the influence of causal thinking. It is difficult to shed one's skin. Our language, in particular, has become completely adapted to that outlook on Nature that Burnet and Gomperz call the Greek one—witness the quotations in the first section. Dozens of vital particles, like *because, as, although, in order to, so that, why, nevertheless, suppose, let alone, all the same,* etc., have assumed a definite logical significance, they have their exact counterparts in all languages that spiritually (not necessarily etymologically) are derived from the Graeco-Roman Mediterranean civilization and make it simple to translate from one language into another. Non-Greek thinking appears from our standpoint and expressed in our language not only as strange, not only as distorted and wrong, but easily as drivel without rhyme or reason. We shall hardly ever really adopt it, but at most use it eclectically to supplement and develop our own mode of thought after we have recognized (following Gomperz) its distinct character and have possibly uncovered gaps which owing to its point of departure it cannot fill by itself.

It is in the nature of the comprehensibility doctrine that in reflecting on the course of events one always brings together in one's mind such perceptions or observations as stand in the relation of necessity to each other. Causal chains are selected and designated as the only thing of consequence. In real life, however, hundreds of causal chains constantly cross each other, and so it happens that events constantly coincide which are not related in an intelligible way and whose coincidence passes for chance in the eyes of those who are scientifically minded. They are matters like a solar eclipse and a lost battle; a black cat which crosses my path from the left and a business misadventure on the same day. But also matters like a train connexion missed in Basle because a dog was run over, which makes me meet an acquaintance from Istanbul the same evening and thereby (logical subject is still the dead dog) turns all my future life into a new direction. Or a gig which passes just as a baby has fallen out of a

second-storey window onto the tip of a lamppost where
its fall is broken by its tearing dress so that it falls then
on the roof of the gig, rolls from there onto the box and
gets away with a lacerated bruise (this last case is taken
from my paternal family chronicle). But even apart from
such exceptional fateful events, anybody who looks closely
at a path of life familiar to him, such as his own, will gain
the impression that random coincidences of events or
circumstances which are not directly causally connected
play a very large, actually the most interesting, part in it;
compared to them the rôle of the transparent causal chains
appears rather trivial, as the mechanism that forms the
vehicle for the actually intended show, the keyboard on
which the often beautiful, often horrible, but ultimately
always somehow meaningful harmony is being played.
And this may lead to the conclusion that the comprehensibility dogma, reasonable as it may appear, still explains
only a small and at that the most trivial part of the interconnexions that really interest us, while the essentials remain uncomprehended.

Sauntering along the ocean beach we may find a dead
fish, a piece of driftwood, and a small stoppered green
bottle washed ashore in close proximity. We may pass
them without paying any heed; or we may be particularly
interested in one or all of these objects; that they happened to lie there together, will start us thinking only if
we surmise a reason for the coincidence, as, e.g., that they
may stem from the same shipwreck. A meditating, but not
yet Westernized, Chinese is inclined to search for a
*meaning* (*tao*) in a fated encounter of indifferent objects
without emotional connotations, not necessarily for a
superstitious meaning; it may fascinate him to ponder such
a small segment of the meaning of Nature at large, which
for him is entirely pervaded by meaning; to contemplate
it perhaps in a purely observant attitude, similar to that of
a Western scholar who encountering a minor experiment
observes and reflects upon it: e.g., water drops which run
down a pane of glass, join, thereupon move faster, decrease in size by losing small fragments, slow down, etc.
He is looking for the law—the other for the meaning. He

may be less concerned with a general law. He contemplates the individual case. Nature exists only once. Each of her actions must have its specific meaning which is to be deciphered from her free, one is tempted to say, artistic, creation, just as in any of the thousands of finely drawn characters of Chinese ideographic writing.

This attitude is foreign to scientific thought which has built large and important disciplines upon the principle that chance is just chance. In Darwin's theory of evolution and in the mechanical theory of heat we have based the occurrence of highly complex events and the explanation of practically inviolable regularities on the principle that chance is 'blind'. I shall soon come back to this point.

## 15. *Renunciations and conventions: induction, causality, initial conditions*

I am not inclined to grant in principle to the taoistic way of thinking equal rights with ours. I believe there is more to it than mere partiality based on habit. To resolve the course of Nature into causal chains is as a method superior to the other procedure in about the same way as our (i.e., the Phoenician) alphabetic writing resolving language into a small number of individual sounds is superior to ideographic writing which does not do so, but tries to embody the meaning more directly in characters agreed upon. It is true that thereby our world-picture, just as our writing, becomes more sober. There is a renunciation involved whose more grievous consequences will become apparent only in the context of the fourth section. Here we shall only briefly indicate the traces of this renunciation as they appear in the edifice of purely scientific thought, where they have occasionally led to lively discussions. We shall introduce them in three stages, proceeding from the general to the specific.

(a) *The law of induction.* Causality in its most cautious, actually in its only admissible, presentation, that of Hume, is nothing but induction from experience. Empirical science is entirely based on it, but induction itself cannot be based on anything, it is suspended in mid air. In short: we find once or more often that after an A a B follows and expect when A recurs that B will do so, too. Why? Well, provided we apply it carefully and not thoughtlessly in a mechanical way, we are usually right in our expectation. But this means only: we have in a great many different cases (i.e., for different pairs of events) ascertained the *permanence of the interconnexion*—and therefore expect it again. This is psychologically quite true; logically it is a circle. The general law of induction is a special case of itself. Though our only signpost in the realm of experience, it itself cannot be based on experience. On what then? (See Sections 11 and 13.)

(b) *The strict law of causality.* Disregarding this difficulty, the physicist formulates the more stringent hypothesis that an exactly defined initial state of a physical system whenever it recurs is always succeeded by precisely the same course of events, precisely the same succession of states. Confronted with the question whether this assumption is true we must, however, admit that even with the most precise means of observation it can in principle not be verified; for Nature is given to us only once and never returns to precisely the same state. It needs, therefore, a rather detailed physical world-picture in which one believes in order to decide in an individual case which changed circumstances (e.g., position of the planet Mars) may reasonably be left out of the consideration.

(c) *The initial conditions.* The strictest formulation of the laws which govern the course of physical events is given by differential equations, ordinary ones if we are dealing with a system of a finite number of degrees of freedom, e.g., a mass point, partial ones in the case of fields. This transparent mathematical formulation represents the cleanest division between that which is covered by the theoretical assertion and that about which the theory refrains from making any assertion at all. It is in the nature of such equations to describe precisely the course of events following a given initial state of the system, but to leave the initial state entirely open; as to which initial states are realized in Nature, nothing is stated and in principle any one is admitted. When applying the equations to an individual case, we must first 'look up Nature' to find out which one is present.

## 16.  *The hypothesis of molecular disorder*

Violent and almost endless debates about the mechanical theory of heat have ensued from the fact that although the overwhelming majority of all the possible initial states of the models of physical systems considered in this theory leads to a course of events *concurring* with experience, yet initial states are conceivable—though in an insignificant minority of cases—that would entail a behaviour in direct contradiction to experience, partly even an entirely irregular one. These have to be excluded by a special supplementary hypothesis. It is not a very unnatural one. What is involved is the exclusion of improbable exceptional cases, just as I do *not* expect when looking up a telephone number to find 77,777 or 55,555—except that the example is *much* too weak.

The supplementary hypothesis went at first under the name of "Stosszahl-ansatz," later under that of 'molecular disorder'. It consists—to be somewhat more explicit—in the exclusion of certain most ingeniously contrived correlations between the positions and the velocities of all atoms at a given time and, if a field is involved, also between the values of the field components in the different points of the region in question. Expressed in this way, the matter appears altogether reasonable and inconsequential, and the occasional heat of the discussion difficult to understand. But it becomes understandable if we add this: as an inexorable consequence of the theory the state of a physical system as it is realized at a given moment actually presents just as ingeniously contrived a scheme of correlations of positions, velocities, and field quantities—just as contrived as those that we had to exclude; and this is a natural consequence of the circumstance that the system has arrived at a given state from former states by a law-determined course. In short, among the states which must be excluded by a supplementary hypothesis, there are also the 'temporal mirror images' (explanation follows) of all those that the theory may admit a posteriori—and even some more. (Explanation: by a 'temporal mirror image' of a state we mean the one for which merely the directions of all velocities and all magnetic field strengths are reversed.)

Because of its importance we have tried to make the matter somewhat intelligible also to the non-physicist. To most people it is hardly disturbing, and rightly so. In this residue, which from the standpoint of pure logic remains unexplained in the theory of heat, we perceive an unmistakable trace of our firm refusal to give account of non-causally determined coincidences.

# IV. GAPS ARISING FROM OBJECTIVATION

## 17. *Some fragments from Heraclitus*

That objectivation, or the 'hypothesis of the real world around us', was a *conscious* step of Ionian natural philosophy, can, I believe, be inferred at least with regard to the 'dark' Heraclitus of Ephesus from some of his rare fragments; I have, though, to assume the sole responsibility for the interpretation attempted here. I am going to consider the matter in somewhat more detail because it furnishes evidence for the fact, often noted, that the views of this oldest phase of Greek thought were more progressive, freer, and more modern in our sense than what their spiritual successors made of it in latter-day atomism.

First of all I must call to mind that at least at the time of Heraclitus it was a matter of course to interpret dream images as reality. Characters that appear in one's dreams —living or dead, or gods—were thought to be actually present, one believed in actual communication with them.

Similar views are still found much later, and not at all only among the 'folk' but—going back to the 'optical theory' of Democritus—in the fanatic pioneers of enlightenment, Epicurus[9] and Lucretius.[10] Fine membranes, formed of atoms which continuously detach themselves from the surface of the bodies and enter the eyes retaining their shape, are supposed to produce not only the immediate visual perceptions but also—note the strange co-ordination—mirror images, hallucinations, and dream images. (Perceptions of smell and sound are similarly explained, only shape is either not conserved or not perceived.) And there can be no doubt that this was meant quite seriously. For later on when it is a question of explaining why the belief in the gods of Graeco-Roman mythology is so widespread, Lucretius calmly declares that the reason is quite plain since these gods from time immemorial have again and again appeared to the mortals, in waking and even more so in dreams, where said *mortals* had ample opportunity to convince themselves of the eternal youth of those *im*mortals.

But now let us proceed to those fragments of Heraclitus, the text of which I quote from Diels.[11]

> D. fr. 2: *diò deî hépesthai tô koinô. toû lógou d' eóntos xunoû zōousin hoi polloì hōs idían échontes phrónēsin*
>
> It is therefore necessary to follow the common. But while reason ("Weltgesetz" according to D.) is common, the majority live as though they had a private insight of their own.

[9] S. Cyril Bailey, *Epicurus* (Oxford 1926), sect. 46a–53 of the letter to Herodotus. Also p. 163, op. cit., sect. 32, *Vita Epicuri* by Diogenes Laertius, who quotes the following as Epicurus's opinion: 'And the visions of the insane and those in dreams are true, for they cause movement, and that which does not exist cannot cause movement.'

[10] *De rerum natura* IV, 26 ff.

[11] Hermann Diels, *Die Fragmente der Vorsokratiker*, 5th ed., Walther Kranz 1934. The numbering of the fragments follows the first edition throughout. The English versions of the fragments are taken from Burnet, John, *Early Greek Philosophy*, A. & C. Black, London 1930.

D. fr. 73: *ou deī hósper katheúdontas poieīn kaì légein; (kaì gàr kaì tóte dokoûmen poieīn kaì légein)*

We must not act and speak like sleepers; (for then in our sleep too we believe that we act and speak).

D. fr. 114: *xùn nóō légontas ischurízesthai chrḕ tō̄ xunō̄ pantōn, hokōsper nómō pólis, kaì polù ischurotéros. tréphontai gàr pántes hoi anthrō̄peioi nómoi hupò henòs tou theíou; krateī gàr tosoûton hókoson ethélei kaì exarkeī pāsi kaì periginetai*

Those who speak with a sound mind must hold fast to what is common to all, just the same as a city holds on to her law, nay, much more strongly so; for all the laws of men are fed by the one divine law. This prevails as much as it will and suffices for all things with a net surplus.

D. fr. 89: *(ho Hē. phēsi) toīs egrēgorósi héna kaì koinòn kósmon eīnai, tòn dè koimōménōn hékaston eis ídion apostéphethai*

The waking have *one* common world, but the sleeping turn aside each into a world of his own.

The strong emphasis in fr. 2 and particularly in fr. 114 on resolutely holding fast to that which is common to all has given rise to amazement. One must know that this man had no socialistic pretensions, but was an aristocrat through and through; he likes to abuse the masses, who do everything wrong, he even abuses (how modern!) most other philosophers, he once says one man of genius is worth to him more than 10,000 average persons. What, then, is this 'common' that deserves so much respect?

I believe that the explanation lies in the fragments 73 and 89. It is meant in the epistemological sense. Heraclitus is well aware that, actually, there is no difference between the sense perceptions in dreams and in waking. The only criterion of reality is being common to all. This is the basis upon which we construct a real world around us. All spheres of consciousness partially overlap—not quite literally, that is impossible, but by means of physical reactions and communications, which we have learned to understand in each other. The overlapping part of the spheres of consciousness forms the world that is common to all. In it there reigns a law, the *lógos* of fr. 2, the *heîs theîos nómos* of fr. 114, which is common to *all* and from which all human laws are derived in so far as they regulate life within a population subject to the natural law once given and immutable. Whoever does not recognize the latter is not *xùn nóō légōn*, but insane; or he acts and talks like a sleeper; for, indeed, in sleep every one turns away from the common world of the waking to his private dream world.

## 18. *The exclusion of the personality*

We have already briefly mentioned in the introduction, Section I, 4(b), that while objectivating the world we imperceptibly remove the cognizing subject from it, and also why we are prone to overlook this circumstance. The scientific thinker is perhaps willing to admit that he removes his own perceiving and thinking self from the world and for the time being assumes the position of an onlooker. But there still remain *all the others* as representatives of the cognizing subject. Since he is after all only one of them and the whole is obviously symmetrical with respect to all, he lets himself slip in again. It would be more correct for him to say that they all remain as much outside as he does; maybe not really, but owing to the simplification adopted to make the construction of a comparatively intelligible objective world at all possible. It is a convention similar to the one by which the citizens of a community agree to submit to a common law. With the one difference that not only may the citizens choose *whether or not* they want to do so, but also what law they want to submit to, within the frame of the natural law which holds for all. For the general convention, the recognition of the real world around us must, of course, have preceded. And only the 'whether' is an object of choice; the content of the law is imposed. That is why Heraclitus calls it a *theîos nómos*. To be sure, it is requested that all *should* submit to this agreement that they would be well-advised to do so—*dei* or *chrè*, an inescapable 'must' would be *anánkē*; but it is a necessary condition for the coexistence of human beings, and whoever refuses to accept it, is just a fool.

One is tempted to compare the theoretical exclusion of the personality in the objectivation of the world to the practical surrender of private interest to the sense of civic duty which submits to the law of the community. But that is only a figure of speech, not an argument.

Incidentally, I do not want to be misunderstood. I do not take the position that in the study of Nature one's own personality *ought* to be excluded, but that it actually *is* excluded in our thinking and that this goes back to the Greeks. It so happens that while I am writing these lines I find my view supported in an article by C. G. Jung[12] in a totally different context and taking an entirely different, almost reproving, attitude. He says in an essay on the "Spirit of Psychology" (Der Geist der Psychologie):

> All science, however, is a function of the soul and all knowledge is rooted in it. It is the greatest of all cosmic wonders and the *conditio sine qua non* of the world as an object. It is extremely strange that the Western world, apart from a very few exceptions, apparently appreciates this fact so little. Behind all the external objects of cognition the subject of all cognition has disappeared into the background, at times to the point of apparent non-existence.

## 19.  *An antinomy of Democritus of Abdera*

We now proceed to the essential part of this whole investigation, i.e., to demonstrate the antinomies that in our opinion arise from the process of exclusion. They are old antinomies which produce, whenever one is reminded of them. fresh embarrassment, bewilderment, uneasiness. Our thesis seems to throw light on them, while they in

[12] *Eranos-Jahrbuch* 1946 (Vol. 14), p. 398; Rheinverlag, Zürich 1947.

their turn support it by the unpleasant fact of their existence.

It is mainly this: neither the immediate sense perceptions, like red, blue, bitter, sweet, resonant . . . nor the consciousness itself of which they are part, appear as such in the objective picture of Nature; they have here formal representatives of a totally different kind, namely, electromagnetic vibrations, frequencies, chemical reactions . . . and the physiological function of the central nervous system. The material representatives have as little in common with the corresponding quality of the mind as the sound of a word in any language with the object of concept denoted by it. For a correct co-ordination one practically needs a special dictionary. Very well: but on the other hand, the whole picture is built up exclusively from sense perceptions and thoughts that take place in the mind (where else?). Where exactly did they get lost? This strange situation was already a puzzle to Democritus (Diels, fr. 125). Galen gives us the following short report: Democritus has expressed his mistrust of the direct evidence of the senses in this way (the translation follows Cyril Bailey):

> *nómō chroiě, nómō glukú, nómō pikrón, eteě ď átoma kai kenón;*
> Colour is by convention, sweet by convention, bitter by convention; in truth there are but atoms and the void;

then he lets the senses speak against the intellect as in a dialectic dialogue:

> *tálaina phrěn, par' hēméōn laboúsa tas písteis hēméas katabálleis? ptómá toi tò katáblēma*
> Wretched mind, from us you are taking the evidence by which you would overthrow us? Your victory is your own fall.

These words could only be written by someone who—even though as scientist he was and remained an atomist—as philosopher was well aware of the epistemological limits, the one-sidedness, and the incompleteness, of his materialistic world-view. The passage was only discovered in 1901 by H. Schöne. It leads us to interpret also some others, which have been known before, as decidedly agnostic, even though this may formerly have met with doubts.

fr. 6: A man must learn on this principle that he is far removed from the truth.

fr. 7: We know nothing truly about anything, but for each of us his opinion is an influx (i.e., is conveyed to him by an influx of 'idols' from without).

fr. 8: To learn truly what each thing is, is a matter of uncertainty.

fr. 9: In truth we know nothing unerringly, but only as it changes according to the disposition of our body, and of the things that enter into it and impinge on it.

fr. 117: We know nothing truly, for the truth lies hidden in the depth.

It is difficult for me to understand that *Gomperz* (*Griechische Denker,* 3rd ed., vol. I, pp. 228 and 454) should maintain in the face of this evidence that Democritus was free of any touch of scepticism. Referring to the dialogue between the intellect and the senses (fr. 125) he remarks: 'One would like to know what Democritus made the intellect reply.' Can one believe Galen capable of withholding the answer, of breaking off this interesting conversation somewhere in the middle? That would practically amount to forgery, although such things are, unfortunately, quite customary—by quoting incompletely. Gomperz supplies the answer to himself: 'Hardly anything else than that mistrust of the senses is called for where their evidence is contradictory (i.e., regarding the secondary qualities); but if their evidence agrees, as with regard to tangible bodies and their primary or fundamental qualities, it remains unassailed and represents the basis of knowledge.' Has this attempted supplementation not perhaps been undertaken in the spirit of—Epicurus? To trust your senses provided there is no contradictory evidence of the senses! Thus: sun, moon, and stars are, since there is no contradictory evidence, about as large as they appear to us. (Cyril Bailey, op. cit., letter to Pythocles, paragraph 91; what is actually meant by the peculiar equating of linear and angular quantities, which Lucretius V. 564 ff. conscientiously repeats, remains to be explained.) At any rate, with respect to Gomperz's conjecture I should like to remark the following—and this was my main reason for quoting it—: the traditional distinction between primary and secondary qualities of matter to-day belongs on the rubbish heap. Bodily dimensions and motions, and, say, so-called impenetrability, are not any more primary than are colour, taste, and sound. If anything deserves the name primary, it is the sense qualities. The geometric picture of matter in space and time is a mental construct, and even, probably very much in need of revision. If one were to make further use of those epithets, they would have to be exactly reversed.

Much more extensively, but in basic agreement with the fragment 125 of Democritus, A. S. Eddington in the introduction to his Gifford lectures (*The Nature of the Physical World*, Cambridge University Press 1928) describes to us his 'two desks', one of them solid and familiar from daily life, at which he sits, which he sees before him, on which he leans his arms, the other one scientific, not only lacking in all sense qualities but in addition full of holes; after all, it consists preponderantly of empty space in which only innumerable, comparatively tiny (i.e., compared to their mutual distances) nuclei and electrons whirl around each other in all directions. Following the impressive juxtaposition of the dear old piece of furniture and the physical model that would have to replace it in a scientific description he remarks:

> In the world of physics we watch a shadowgraph performance of the drama of familiar life. The shadow of my elbow rests on the shadow table as the shadow ink flows over the shadow paper. . . . The frank realisation that physical science is concerned with a world of shadows is one of the most significant of recent advances.

I like to put this quotation side by side with one from the marvelous Gifford Lectures of Charles Sherrington,[13] a book which will become a landmark in the history of philosophy and which reveals more clearly and at the same time more cautiously than had ever been done before what knowledge is to-day available of the relation between mind and body and what ideas one may reasonably form on this matter. I am referring to the passage on p. 357 which reads:

> Mind, for anything perception can compass, goes therefore in our spatial world more ghostly than a ghost. Invisible, intangible, it is a thing not even of outline; it is not a 'thing'. It remains without sensual confirmation, and remains without it for ever.

One of the two thus seems irrevocably doomed to a ghostlike existence, either the objective external world of the scientist, or the self of consciousness which by thinking constructs the former, withdrawing from it in the process.

## 20. *The paradox of free will*

Sherrington's remark refers, in particular, to the circumstance that nowhere in the course of physiological processes do we encounter the point where consciousness, mind, thinking, or will, exerts the immediate directing influence, so well known from inner experience, on the train of events. In these lectures, Sherrington again and again is concerned about this same matter in many pages of fascinating, sensitive, careful discussion. Plucking out individual sentences does not give an adequate impression; however, I am going to quote two passages chosen almost at random:

> physical science . . . faces us with the impasse that mind *per se* cannot play the piano—mind *per se* cannot move a finger of a hand. (p. 222)
> Then the impasse meets us. The blank of the 'how'

[13] *Ch. Sherrington, Man on his Nature*, Cambridge University Press 1940.

of mind's leverage on matter. The inconsequence stag-
gers us. Is it a misunderstanding? Another is not uncon-
nected with it.[14] (p. 232)

The paradox is so painful that it is always meeting with
the violent resistance of those who hope to solve it by
denying it. This is why we have chosen to refer to the
past master of physiology of our time, even though it
appears to us that this is not a matter of experience, but
something that is inherent in the conventional structure of
our world-picture. Indeed, Spinoza, for example, who had
only an insignificant fraction of Sherrington's physiological
insight at his disposal, has expressed the thesis so in-
cisively and resolutely that it is impossible—provided its
correctness is admitted—to speak of a 'prescient intuition'.

> Nec corpus mentem ad cogitandum nec mens corpus
> ad motum neque ad quietem nec ad aliquid (si quid
> est) aliud determinare potest. (*Ethics*, P. III, Prop. 2).
> The body cannot determine the soul to thought, nor
> can the soul determine the body to motion or rest, or to
> anything else (if there be anything else).

We attribute the situation to the distinguishing features
of the scientific world-picture. Because it contains at the
outset the implicit renunciation of inclusion of the thinker's
own person, and because it is quite essentially based on
this renunciation, it becomes confused if one tries to re-
store that person. The comprehensibility of the picture
does not permit any deviation from the compelling necessity with which in the spatio-temporal course of events
each successive stage is determined by the previous one.
Therefore, there is no room for the interference of the
mind in controlling the events, and we are caught up short
by the antinomy of determinism and free will which in this
form is insoluble.

Perhaps Democritus already had sensed this; in any
event, he remained firm, convinced that in this case there
is no *corriger la fortune*. Not so latter-day atomism, as
was already shown in Section 6 in more detail. The at-

[14] The quotation will be continued below at the proper place.

tempt to save the situation has lately been repeated in modern guise by some quantum physicists. From the standpoint of physics it has to be rejected since, even assuming the fundamental laws to be purely statistical, they would be sent tumbling, just as strictly causal ones, by arbitrary acts of demons.

Perhaps some will voice the frequently heard objection: if you reject everything that might mitigate inexorable determinism, what shall you reply to the criminal who uses as an excuse that he is only an automaton and not responsible for his actions? To this one may first reply that in regulating civil life we cannot afford the luxury of excluding the personality, much rather can we afford a violation of the consistency of science. But if anyone still wants to maintain the latter and hence deduce that he is suffering an injustice, he should consider that in that case the lawmaker, the judge, the policeman, and the prison guard also act according to unalterable necessity and, therefore, do as little right or wrong as an avalanche or an earthquake.

## 21. *The Masque of the Red Death*

We are thus facing the following strange situation. While all building stones for the world-picture are furnished by the senses qua organs of the mind, while the world-picture itself is and remains for everyone a construct of his mind and apart from it has no demonstrable existence, the mind itself remains a stranger in this picture, it has no place in it, it can nowhere be found in it. We are usually not aware of this. We are so used, in our thoughts, to inserting the personality of a human being—that of an animal for that matter—into his body that we are amazed to learn and are doubtful and hesitant about believing that in reality it is not there. We place it in the head, a good bit behind the center of the eyes. From there it looks at us, as it may be, with understanding, loving, soulful, suspicious, or angry eyes. Has it ever occurred to anyone that the eye is the only one among the sense organs whose receptive character the naïve person does not recognize; reversing the situation he is much rather inclined to think of visual rays emanating from the eye than of light rays emitted from objects impinging on it. One finds this 'visual ray' not seldom in cartoons, even in older sketches of popular physics, as a dotted line drawn from the eye *to* the object, which latter is indicated by an arrow pointing to it at the far end. And, dear [father] reader, or still better, dear [mother] reader, think of the 'shining eyes' with which your child 'beams' at you when you have brought him a new toy; and then let the physicist tell you that, in reality, *nothing* emanates from those eyes—they are continuously bombarded by light quanta—that is their way of functioning. In reality. Strange reality. Something seems to be missing from it.

It is quite difficult for us to realize that the localization of the personality in the body is meant symbolically, for practical use only. If we follow the soulful look into the interior with the knowledge we possess of it, we encounter indeed highly interesting, incredibly complicated, doings: billions of cells of very specialized structure in a vast and complex arrangement, yet evidently aimed at extensive mutual communication; throbbing electric impulses, pulsating incessantly, yet in rapidly changing distribution, conducted from nerve cell to nerve cell, while at each instant tens of thousands of contacts are being formed or blocked; chemical reactions going on simultaneously; all this and much more we encounter, and eventually we may discover impulses flowing through long cellular processes, motor nerve fibres, to certain arm muscles which then extend the hand, hesitating and trembling, to bid a long farewell, while other impulses stimulate a secretion of glands and tears blur the sad eye. Nowhere on the way, however, do we encounter the personality, nowhere the heartache and the anxiety that move this soul and of whose reality we are as certain as if we ourselves were suffering them—as we do. It is really true that the physiological analysis of any human being, even of our closest friend, reveals the same sight to us as in E. A. Poe's masterpiece *The Masque of the Red Death* is revealed to the bold one who insolently tears away from the masker his cloak and domino and underneath finds—nothing. For are nerve cells and electric currents anything more, where it is for us a matter of emotional values and the experience of the soul? When we first realize it, we may be shaken. But we shall soon overcome the shock if we consider that the same reasoning applies to ourselves, and yet, we *are;* since we think, as Descartes put it. There are even moments when it may be a relief to think that the now lifeless body was only symbolically and never in reality the seat of the soul we are now longing for.

Actually, one can say in a few words why our perceiving and thinking self is nowhere to be found *within* the world-picture: because it itself *is* this world-picture. It is identical with the whole and, therefore, cannot be contained in it as a part. It is true: there seem to be many such conscious selves; the world, however, exists but once. This arithmetic dilemma goes back to the history of its formation, or rather, to the formation of the *concept* of the world. The contents of the individual spheres of consciousness partly overlap. The domain common to all of them, Heraclitus's *koinón* or *xunón,* represents the world of the sane and waking to which they must hold fast, like the citizens of a community to their protecting law, in order not to be considered, or to become, insane. Whoever mistakes his hallucinations or his dream images for reality, we call insane.

## 22. *Attempts at a solution: monadology, doctrine of identity*

There are two ways out of the numerical dilemma, both of which seem, indeed, insane within the framework of Greek scientific thinking. One of them is the multiplication of the world in Leibniz's awful doctrine of monads: each monad a world to itself, without windows; that they agree is pre-established harmony. There are, I believe, few people who think in such a way that they find this solution to their liking, or even see in it a mitigation of the antinomy.

The opposite alternative is the unification of minds. The multiplicity is only apparent. This is the doctrine of the Upanishads. And not of the Upanishads only. The mystical experience of the union with God regularly leads to this view, unless strong prejudices stand in its way, and, therefore, more easily in the East than in the West.

> At the death of every living being the spirit returns to the world of spirits and the body to the world of bodies. But only the bodies change in this process. The world of spirits is a single spirit standing like a light in back of the world of bodies and shining through each individual that comes into existence as through a window. According to the kind and size of the window, more or less light penetrates into the world. But the light always remains the same.[15]

This world-view possesses even more than others the distinctive feature that one cannot talk about it in a matter-of-fact way, free of allegories, but only in metaphors. Whoever considers this a defect, had better not waste any time on it. A very extensive exposition has recently appeared in English, based on an extremely copious and truly invaluable anthology selected from the documents of the so-called mystics of all ages and countries.[16] In general, however, this alternative does not satisfy Western thinking any more than does that of Leibniz. It is not appropriate to it. After all, it is quite non-Greek in its origin. Just the same, the doctrine of identity is in one respect ahead of monadology. It can point out that empirically the mind is always given in the singular. Let us consider this point a little more closely even though it means a digression in the framework of this study. But it

[15] The words stem from the Persian-Islamic mystic Azīz Nasafī of the 13th century A.D. See Fritz Meyer, *Eranos-Jahrbuch* 1946, p. 190 f. (Rheinverlag, Zürich 1947).

[16] Aldous Huxley, *The Perennial Philosophy*, Chatto & Windus, London 1946.

is just the place where I really feel the Greek-scientific thinking to be in need of a correction, of a 'blood transfusion from the East'.[17]

## 23. The unity of the mind

The mind, I maintain, is something which we simply cannot conceive of in the plural. Even in the pathological cases of split personalities the two persons alternate, they do not simultaneously dominate the scene.[18] And if, in the puppet play of dreams, I am holding the strings of the action and speech of a host of actors in my hands, I do not know about it. Only one of them is myself. Through him I act and speak directly while waiting anxiously and eagerly for what somebody else is going to reply, whether or not he is going to do me the favour I am asking for. I do not realize that actually I can make him do and speak as I want—although that is not true either. For this 'other person' is in such cases usually the embodiment of a difficulty that confronts me in waking life and over which I have, indeed, no control.

I simply cannot imagine how my unitary mind should either have developed by integration of the minds of the cells—or of some of them—that constitute my body or

[17] I have pointed this out in the epilogue to my little book *What Is Life?*, Cambridge University Press 1944 (pp. 1–88 in the present volume).

[18] In his paper quoted above (*Der Geist der Psychologie*, op. cit., p. 392) C. G. Jung reports, however (following Janet, *Automatisme Psychologique*, 1913, p. 243, 238 ff.), on a case of split personality: 'But Janet has established that while one of the consciousnesses so to speak dominated the mind, the other simultaneously communicated with the observer by way of a code expressed in motions of the fingers. Dual consciousness can thus quite well exist simultaneously.'

It does not seem to me that this is in contradiction to what I have in mind. Interesting as the case is, it only demonstrates that the observer of two widely separated spheres of consciousness was able to perceive their manifestations simultaneously. This is experienced by anybody who is in simultaneous conversation with two people. Dual consciousness need not be experienced as such by the subject concerned. To my mind it is impossible, almost a contradiction in terms.

form at each instant their resultant, as it were, unless it were one at the outset and by its very nature. Such a cellular organization as each of us represents should, one would imagine, prove an occasion *par excellence* for the mind to manifest multiplicity provided it were at all capable of it. For the time is long since past when the expression 'cellular organization' was a mere figure of speech. The physiologist tells us:[19]

> To declare that, of the component cells which go to make us up, each one is an individual self-centred life, is no mere phrase. It is not a mere convenience for descriptive purposes. The cell as a component of the body is not only a visibly demarcated unit but a unit-life centred on itself. It leads its own life. . . . The cell is a unit-life, and our life which in its turn is a unitary life consists utterly of the cell-lives.

This idea can be expressed even more concretely. Brain pathology as well as sense-physiology investigations point quite definitely to a regional division of the sensorium into areas whose extensive independence amazes us because, this being the case, one would naïvely expect that independent spheres of consciousness correspond to them. If we regard a landscape first through both eyes as usual, then close the right eye, and then the left, there is practically no difference. The psychic visual space is in all three cases identically the same. This could very well be due to the conduction of stimuli from corresponding retinal points to the same central physiological mechanism which 'takes care of perception'. But from investigations of binocular flicker frequencies it follows unambiguously that this is not so. These experiments lead to a conclusion which we shall reproduce here in part:[20]

> It is not spatial conjunction of cerebral mechanism which combines them (sc. the two reports). . . . It is much as though the right- and left-eye images were seen each by one of two observers and the minds of

[19] C. Sherrington, op. cit., p. 73.
[20] C. Sherrington, op. cit., pp. 273–75.

the two observers were combined to a single mind. It is as though the right-eye and left-eye perceptions are elaborated singly and then psychically combined to one. . . . It is as if each eye had a separate sensorium of considerable dignity proper to itself, in which mental processes based on that eye were developed up to even full perceptual levels. Such would amount physiologically to a visual sub-brain. There would be two such sub-brains, one for the right eye and one for the left. Contemporaneity of action rather than structural union seems to provide their mental collaboration.

Subsequently follow general considerations from which I can only select these characteristic sentences:[21]

Are there thus quasi-independent sub-brains based on the several modalities of sense? In the roof-brain the old 'five' senses instead of being merged inextricably in one another and further submerged under mechanism of higher order are still plain to find, each demarcated in its separate sphere. How far is the mind a collection of quasi-independent perceptual minds integrated psychically in large measure by temporal concurrence of experience? . . . When it is a question of 'mind' the nervous system does not integrate itself by centralization upon one pontifical cell. Rather it elaborates a million-fold democracy whose each unit is a cell. . . . The concrete life compounded of sub-lives reveals, although integrated, its additive nature and declares itself an affair of minute foci of life acting together. . . . When however we turn to the mind there is nothing of all this. The single nerve-cell is never a miniature brain. The cellular constitution of the body need not be for any hint of it from 'mind'. . . . A single pontifical brain-cell could not assure to the mental reaction a character more unified and non-atomic than does the roof-brain's multitudinous sheet of cells. Matter and energy seem granular in structure, and so does 'life', but not so mind.

[21] Pp. 275–78.

This terminates our excursion into a domain outside the limits that we have marked out for ourselves.

## 24. *The dual rôle of the thinking subject*

Even more embarrassing than the above antinomies is the incongruity between the subjective primacy of the mind which with some reason considers itself to be everything there is, and the comparatively minor rôle that is accorded to its carrier or 'representative' in the picture of the external world. According to this one would have to think of the consciousness, the mind, or what have you (Lat. *mens,* Germ. *Bewusstsein*) as something arisen on our planet in the course of organic evolution and, indeed, one almost receives the impression of what in French would be called *'un accident'*: something that might just as well not have taken place. 'Man's mind is a recent product of our planet's side'.[22]

Phylogenetically, the brain starts as a bulge, a lateral protuberance somewhere on the stimuli-transmitting nerve pathway which leads from the energy receiver—the primitive sense organ—to the motor end-plate of the reflex arc, i.e., to the point where as a result of the stimulus the organism acts on its environment. The thickening delays this effect and by communicating with other similar protuberances in other reflex arcs it makes possible an adaptation of the total response to the changing total situation of the environment. One might say, it is a matter of coordinating the single reflexes, which to start with are correlated with single stimuli, and of building up from them a scheme which correlates a more or less composite organic arrangement of reflexes with each *constellation* of stimuli that appear simultaneously at different entry points. One should immediately add that the group of stimuli that determine the released reflex need not be quite simultaneous. Rather, very soon the highly signifi-

[22] Compare, for the following, Chapter VII, The Brain and Its Work, in Sherrington's book, in particular p. 213 ff. Above sentence p. 218.

cant achievement is attained that the traces of earlier stimuli also take part in determining the motor effect; i.e., memory, and learning—which memory renders possible—make their appearance.

This, then, was the beginning. A regulating organ. A special device to co-ordinate motor reactions, a precision tool enabling them to deal effectively with the uncontrollably changing events of the environment and to adapt to them instantly. No matter what immensely complex further development this ingenious trick, this superb invention of Nature, has experienced—it still remains something special. Nor did it at the outset play the overwhelming rôle superior to all other methods that it plays to-day in the higher vertebrates. The tiny—if I am not mistaken, walnut-size—brain of the gigantic saurians is frequently mentioned as a curiosity. Nor is the method unique, it has counterparts. Even in man the purely chemical method of inner hormone secretion has a similar function. It, too, is a regulating device, although a slower, less detailed one, and acting rather summarily. It is highly remarkable that this second regulating device also exerts such a strong and immediate influence on the manifest personality, as is well-known, in particular from diseases of the thyroid and from sexual life.[23]

It seems strange, even contradictory, that we are to think that the perceiving, conscious mind, in which alone the process of the world is mirrored, only made its appearance some time during this process, and as one should say, *incidentally*, as a concomitant to a special biological measure whose task it evidently was to make it easier for certain forms of life to hold their ground in their environment, and so to favour their survival and propagation. That is, for certain, relatively late forms of life. Life capable of holding its own had already existed on earth for a long time. Only a small part took this particular road of providing itself with a brain. And before that happened was everything a play before empty seats? But is not even

[23] A fascinating popular account is found in V. H. Mottram, *The Physical Basis of Personality*, Pelican Books (A 139) 1944.

'that' saying too much about a world that nobody is looking at? We spoke before of the ruins of a city which we excavate, and how we reconstruct from them and other things handed down from the past a picture of its flourishing. It has reality value for us, we believe in it. What actually interests us, is human life, actions, thoughts, feelings, joy and sorrow, which came to pass there. That, we say, was real. But a world that is supposed to have existed for many millions of years without being perceived by any mind whatever, is it anything at all? *Was* it? Let us not forget: if we spoke above of the world process being mirrored in the perceiving mind, this was a stereotype, a phrase, a metaphor, which has achieved general sanction. The world is given only *once*. Nothing is mirrored. Original and mirror image are one. The world extended in space and time is our idea. That it may be something else in addition, is certainly not sustained by experience— as Bishop Berkeley already knew.

The romance of a world teeming with life which only after millions of years of unobserved existence had incidentally the brilliant idea of providing itself with brains and of viewing itself in them, has a sequence. I should like to describe it in the words of Sherrington which immediately follow a passage quoted above (p. 233):

> The universe of energy is we are told running down. It tends fatally towards an equilibrium which shall be final. An equilibrium in which life cannot exist. Yet life is being evolved without pause. Our planet in its surround has evolved it and is evolving it. And with it evolves mind. If mind is not an energy-system how will the running down of the universe affect it? Can it go unscathed? Always so far as we know the finite mind is attached somehow to a running energy-system. When that energy-system ceases to run what of the mind which runs with it? Will the universe which elaborated and is elaborating the finite mind then let it perish?

The mind or consciousness plays a confusing dual rôle.

On the one hand, it is the stage and the only one on which the entire course of the world is taking place, the vessel that contains everything and apart from which there is nothing. On the other hand, we gain the impression, perhaps mistakenly, that within this bustle of the world it is linked to certain very particular organs which are certainly the most interesting objects that animal and plant physiology knows, but still not unique, not *sui generis,* because after all they serve, like so many others, the survival of their carriers, and they owe their formation in the selective process of the evolution of the species to the fact that they do just that.

Occasionally it happens that a painter puts into his big canvas or a poet into his poem an insignificant subordinate figure which is he himself. Most likely, the author of the *Odyssey* thus put himself modestly into his epic as the blind bard who sings of Troy in the hall of the Phaeacians and moves the sorely-tried hero to tears. In the Nibelungenlied we encounter on the march through the Austrian parts a poet whom we suspect of being the author. In Dürer's All Saints picture two large circles of Believers are gathered in adoration around the Trinity floating high up in the clouds, one circle of the saved in heaven, one of the mortals on earth. Kings, emperors, and popes among them. And if I remember correctly, the artist himself is kneeling in the circle of mortals, a modest subsidiary figure that could as well have been left out.

This seems to me the best allegory for the confusing dual rôle of the mind: on the one hand, it is the artist who has created it all, but in the picture, he is an insignificant part of the stage-set, which might as well be missing without making a dent in the total effect.

Without using allegories we must state that we are dealing here with one of the typical antinomies which result from the fact that at least up to now we have not succeeded in constructing an intelligible world-picture, except at the price of the spectator's and architect's withdrawing from it and no longer finding any room in it. The attempt to force him in nevertheless leads to absurdity.

## 25. *Values, meaning and purpose*

Just as the space-time model of the world is colourless, silent, and intangible, i.e., lacking in the sense qualities, so it is lacking in everything and anything the meaning of which lies exclusively in its relation to the conscious, perceiving and feeling self. I am referring particularly to the ethical and aesthetic values, values of any kind, anything that refers to meaning and purpose of the course of events. Not only is all this lacking, it can't even be fitted in organically. If one tries to put it in, as a child colours his black-and-white colouring book, it does not fit. For everything that enters into *this* world-picture willy-nilly takes the form of a scientific proposition; and as such it becomes false.

Life in itself is valuable. 'Respect for life', so I believe did Albert Schweitzer formulate the basic tenet of all morality. Nature does not respect life. She deals with it as if it were the least valuable thing in the world. Produced millionfold, its greatest part is speedily destroyed or becomes prey to other living organisms. That is the master-method to develop new forms of life. 'Thou shalt not torture. Do not cause pain.' Nature knows nothing of it. For survival her creatures depend on torturing each other in continuous struggle.

'There is nothing either good or bad but thinking makes it so.' Nothing that happens in Nature is in itself good or bad. Nor is it beautiful or ugly. The *values* are lacking. The values and, in particular, meaning and purpose. Nature does not act according to purpose. If we speak of purposeful adaptation of an organism to its environment, we know that it is only a convenient figure of speech. If we take it literally we err. We err in the framework of our world-picture, in which there are only strictly causal connexions.

Least of all can we detect a meaning of *the whole* by purely scientific examination. The closer we look the more meaningless it appears. The spectacle which is enacted evidently obtains a meaning only in relation to the contemplating mind. But what science tells us about the character of this relation is without rhyme or reason: as if the mind had only evolved through this same spectacle which it perceives now, and were to vanish with it when the sun has cooled off and the earth has become a desert of rock and ice.

## 26.  *The atheism of natural science*

Let us finally remember that in this context belongs also the notorious atheism of natural science with which the theists reproach it time and again. Unjustly. A personal God cannot have a place in a world-picture that only became accessible at the price of removing from it everything personal. We know that whenever God is experienced, He is an experience as real as an immediate sense perception, as real as one's own personality. Just like the latter He must be absent from the spatial-temporal picture. 'I do not encounter God in space and time', so speaks the honest scientific thinker and is taken to task for it by those in whose catechism it says: God is spirit.

# The Spirit of Science

## 1

The spirit is to an eminent degree subject and thus evades objective examination. It is the subject of cognition (Schopenhauer) and therefore strictly speaking can never be its object.

Permit me to read you a few passages from Shankara's famous commentary on the Vedanta-sutras; it treats of this matter far more clearly than many modern philosophers, not to mention scientists. The English version is by F. Max Müller.[1]

> As it is well known . . . that object and subject, which fall under the perception of *We* and *You* (or, as we should say, of the Ego and Non-Ego), are in their very essence opposed to each other like darkness and light, and that therefore one cannot take the place of the other, it follows all the more that their attributes also cannot be interchanged.

In his commentary on this passage, Max Müller writes: 'Thus for example the Non-Ego can be seen, heard, felt, but the Ego can never be seen, heard, felt. Its nature is to know, not to be known.'

Shankara continues:

> Therefore we may conclude that to transfer what is

[1] *Three Lectures on the Vedanta Philosophy* (London, 1894), pp. 62 ff.

objective, that is what is perceived as *You*, the Non-Ego and its qualities, on what is subjective, that is what is perceived as *We*, the Ego, which consists of thought, or vice versa to transfer what is subjective on what is objective, must be altogether wrong.

In this sense all science is a doctrine of the objective, of the non-ego. It has played such a subordinate part in Hindu thought that among thinkers who equal Plato, Spinoza, or Kant in depth and magnificence of conception, we find utterly childlike and naïve views concerning the objective universe, although their people had dwelt in it for just as long, and they were in the same position for observing it as Western scientists. However, this should not surprise us. It was simply not their concern. The eminent goal of their contemplation was the 'ego that consists of thought,'[2] the ego and its relation to the godhead.

Perhaps we may be permitted to designate this 'ego that consists of thought' as 'spirit', even if it involves us in a controversy with Vedanta scholars regarding 'ego', 'spirit', 'soul', 'reason', etc.

The German language—and only the German language—sets up an antithesis between the *natural* sciences and the *Geisteswissenchaften* (sciences of the spirit, or cultural sciences). This is not fully acceptable, any more than the usage of the Romance peoples and the English, who limit the old universal *scientia* to the natural sciences, and withhold it from philology, history, etc.—as though in these fields there were no *scire* at all.

The German usage is unacceptable, because it reverses the Vedantist's profound distinction between subject and object, between spirit and objective fact; because in both cases it cuts through living flesh at right angles to the organic dividing line.

The object that we can examine scientifically is in every case limited to the non-self, the object as Shankara calls

[2] Compare to this the words of the Buddha: 'All that we are is the result of what we have thought: It is founded on our thoughts, it is made up of our thoughts.' F. Max Müller, *Introduction to the Science of Religion* (London, 1873), p. 24.

it, the object *kat' exochēn*. And the method of scientific
inquiry is always that of natural science, adapted to the
particular type of object. The philologist today sees language as a living organism, developing in a social and
political environment. The methods of comparative philology are almost interchangeable with those of palaeobiol-
ogy. Not to mention those of the psychologist.

Thus the ego, the spirit, can never strictly speaking be
the object of scientific inquiry, because objective knowledge of the spirit is a contradiction in terms. Yet, on the
other hand, all knowledge relates to the spirit, or more
properly, exists in it, and this is the sole reason for our
interest in any field of knowledge whatsoever. The knowledge, or at least the intuition, of this circumstance is indeed as old as the urge for knowledge itself. The naïve
and the natural attitude is to conceive of everything in
relation to ourselves, to our own Ego. But this naïve attitude was for a time submerged beneath our unfortunate
scientific materialism. The sudden and spectacular progress of natural science deluded some of its most brilliant
exponents into supposing that science was about to throw
light on everything that was worth knowing, that outside
of science nothing of the slightest interest would remain,
and, above all, that science would soon solve the 'problem
of the spirit' with a fully objective picture of the thinking
process. Perhaps the submersion of the naïve, natural, and
philosophically sound relation of all knowledge to the
universal human ego (which is the subject of all knowledge but is itself not susceptible to scientific inquiry)
resulted in part from a process of inhibition. The intellectual relation of knowledge to the self was thrust aside by
a physical relation. Through its technical by-products that
often bordered on the miraculous, the knowledge of nature
often proved serviceable to the physical Ego. Thus a
material 'Egoism' took the place of an ideal 'Egoism', and
perhaps helped many people to forget that the ideal Ego
was being submerged.

The object of all science is nature in the broadest sense,
i.e., our spatial and temporal environment in all its aspects.
The subject of every science is always the spirit and—to

vary a well-known saying of Kant—it contains only as much true science as it does spirit.

This insight is valuable in a twofold sense. First, we shall not, in concerning ourselves with the spirit, fall into the error of the Hindus and disregard the natural sciences as though they were utterly irrelevant. True, the spirit is not their object, but this does not mean that they are any less concerned with it than the *Geisteswissenschaften*. For the spirit is never the object of science. But the sciences are a product of the spirit in which they are conducted.

On the other hand, we shall not expect the natural sciences to give us direct insight into the nature of the spirit; we shall not *hope* to penetrate it, however much we learn about the physics and chemistry of the bodily processes with which we find perception and thought objectively linked; and we shall not *fear* that even the most exact knowledge of the mechanism of these processes and the laws by which they operate—a knowledge the subject of which is and will always remain the spirit—can lay fetters upon the spirit itself, that is, can compel us to regard it as unfree, 'mechanically determined', on the ground that it is linked with a physiological process that is mechanically determined and subject to laws of nature. Such an inference would be a *parábasis eis állo génos*, a transference of the qualities of the object to the subject, such as Shankara rightly stigmatizes as absolutely false.

## 2

After what I have said, it is evident that I shall not attempt to analyse objectively the 'spirit of science'. Instead, I shall try merely to put you as subjects in direct contact with those currents of thought which, it seems to me, have determined the development of the sciences in the last ninety or one hundred years. At first it may seem to you that I am merely picking out random examples; but I shall endeavour to show the common forces at work in remotely separate fields, and finally to compose the various trends of thought into a unified picture, a unified spiritual current. Perhaps I may be permitted to state at the outset that in this endeavour I myself—and this should scarcely seem surprising—shall be guided by this same basic force, this same basic trend, for it is nothing other than the increasing simplification and unification of our view of the physical universe. To make myself perfectly clear, I repeat that the endeavour to disclose a common, homogeneous basis in all the broad realms of scientific research is today particularly relevant, because this basic motiv is itself simplification and unification.

To an observer outside the field of science, the contrary seems rather to be the case. Indeed it has become almost a commonplace to say that the more we learn and know, the richer but also the more complex the picture must become. Let us take physics, which would indeed have to constitute the basis for a real unification, for it forms, as it were, the alphabet at the base of all scientific discourse concerning the higher structures: the cosmos, the organism. What additions have been made to this alphabet in the last hundred years and at what a headlong pace! Magnetism, and with it the more exact knowledge of electrical phenomena. The phenomena of refraction and interference in light, so much more complex than Newton had imagined. Electromagnetic waves. Cathode rays. X-rays. Finally, radioactivity, so perplexing at first, with its three or four different types of rays that appeared to be of an entirely new kind, and the strange transformations of one type of matter into another. Hardly had all these developments been to some degree gathered into a system, hardly had scientists begun to hope that they might be able to manage with two types of fundamental particle, the light negative and heavy positive atom of electricity (electron and proton) and one type of waves, the electromagnetic, when first the quantum theory was 'forced upon' us, with its odd conception that energy is transmitted discontinuously. Shortly thereafter we learned from Einstein that energy and matter were one and the same thing. Thus our old particles of matter were themselves quanta of energy, and the energy quanta in light waves had, in turn, to be regarded as a kind of particle. The subsequent development of the quantum theory into 'wave mechanics' showed

—and experiments made it increasingly certain—that there are not, as formerly supposed, two distinct types of radiation, one consisting of waves, the other of particles, but that every type of radiation must be regarded in some respects as a series of waves, in another as a stream of particles, difficult as it may be for our imagination to combine such contradictory characteristics.

So we had a third elementary particle, the atom of light, to which we gave the name of photon. It is only a slight exaggeration to say that from then on scarcely a year passed without the invention or discovery of some new kind of particle—or new kind of hybrid I should say, for each one, of course, was at the same time a variety of wave. Anderson photographed a particle which was unmistakably a light, positive particle, the exact counterpart of the electron. It is now known as positron. A negative heavy particle (as counterpart of the positive proton) is not known, but there is an uncharged heavy particle, the neutron. A light neutral particle has never been found, but was invented and called the neutrino. Then particles of medium mass came to light, positive, negative, and neutral, and these were collectively called mesons, while the uncharged ones are sometimes called neutrettos. Agreement has not yet been reached concerning the exact mass of these mesons; according to what I heard last month[3] in Cambridge, there may be a whole assortment of different masses.

I might continue at length about these developments, but I think I have said enough along these lines. Surely you realize that this brief, incomplete, and 'spiritless' list is not intended to reveal the spirit of modern physics, but rather its seeming lack of spirit. Instead of physics, I might equally well have invoked the example of biology to show that natural science, left to itself, has a tendency to become more and more complicated and 'spiritless'. The number of species described has, I am told, reached the million mark, and grows each year by about twenty thousand. In the rapidly developing field of genetics and

[3] [In July, 1946.—ED.]

the related study of cytology, the originally so simple Mendelian laws have had to be considerably modified and complicated, from year to year new concepts arise, and the resultant terminology has left that of physics far behind both as to bulk and as to demands on Greek and Latin lexicography.

But enough of such examples. You need only open any work, any dissertation on a scientific subject, to convince yourselves how involved the discipline in question has become, and how unintelligible the technical terminology has grown to be for the layman. Let us now try to find the few broad lines along which the spirit is advancing towards simplification and unification of the general picture. Here the kinship of the motive and of the nature of the success that we encounter in widely remote ranges of research reveals to us that the spirit has indeed been active and productive in guiding scientific inquiry, that science has done more than list the answers to the questions asked of nature through experiments: that it has done more than piece together long, elaborate chains of electrons, protons, photons, neutrons, mesons, neutrettos, and neutrinos.

I shall give a brief outline of what I take to be the leading ideas of modern natural science.

In the nineteenth century:

1. Darwinism.
2. Statistical-mechanical theory of heat.

In the twentieth century:

3. Genetics.
4. Quantum theory.
5. Theory of relativity.

From their intersection arise:

6. The problem of time (from 2, 5, and 4).
7. The cosmic problem of astronomy (from 5 and 4).
8. The physical substratum of life and thought (in which 1–4 meet with the chemistry of enzymes and viruses).

It goes without saying that I shall not 'dispose of' this program today.

3

In the analysis of ideas, scientific ideas in any case, it is not always desirable to follow the order of their historical appearance. Often we enter the unknown edifice of a new scientific discipline through a lesser gate that leads us into a side passage; it may take us a long while to find our way to the main portal and view the whole structure in its proper perspective. But apart from this, even the briefest step-by-step account of the development indicated in the above outline would in almost each case exceed the time allotted to my lecture. Moreover, this is not my appointed task; but rather, to indicate the basic, unifying ideas. Here I must ask your indulgence, for my undertaking is exceedingly difficult, and that for two entirely different reasons. The first is that in some of these matters I do not feel justified in assuming that the majority of my listeners possess even the most superficial knowledge of the facts and the ideas based on them. The second is that in hardly a single one of these disciplines is the development concluded. For the most part, beginning, say, with No. 3, we are still in the midst of developments. My work is therefore bound to be fragmentary, and I shall be quite glad if I succeed in giving you a clear idea of two or three of the fascinating leitmotivs.

Let us begin with the nineteenth century. If, scientifically speaking, I call it the century of Darwin and Boltzmann, I follow Ludwig Boltzmann himself, the actual founder of the statistical-mechanical theory (it is ordinarily called thermodynamics but it is far more). Boltzmann once (1886) declared very emphatically that his century would some day be designated not as the century of steam, electricity, the telegraph, the telephone, etc., but as the century of Darwin. He said Darwin. We can hardly expect him to have said Darwin and Boltzmann, but we may be permitted to wonder whether he surmised as much.

The boundless admiration of Boltzmann for Darwin's work points to a common trait in their thoughts and aims. What is that common trait?—In an article commemorating

Boltzmann[4] I have pointed to the statistical law of averages as this common trait which constitutes the backbone, the vital nerve, of both theories. In this, one might see merely a common instrument, akin to the hammer, which is used both by the shoemaker and the stonemason, though for entirely different purposes. But here the common trait is something far more profound. It is a spiritual trend, a trend towards rationality that emerges in the thinking of the century and finds in these two men its highest exponents, a trend that is today still fighting for complete acceptance, though already it has far more supporters than adversaries.

How shall I characterize this trend? Half a dozen phrases come to my lips, yet none of them fully comprehends the matter. Divesting nature of its mystery. Banishment of mysterious natural forces, not to mention teleological traits, from the picture of nature. Repudiation of illusory verbal explanations.—To state the matter more positively: it begins to appear that we are now able to give a common-sense explanation of certain universal and dominant traits of the natural process, where this seemed inherently impossible, where we seemed to have reached the limit of the explicable, where it appeared that we could no longer hope for anything more than a complete description of our findings: we find it to be so and so, but why it is so I cannot tell you; the question itself is perhaps without real meaning (!).

Here I cannot go into details. But you know that according to the Darwinian theory the species arise and are transformed *de facto* along lines of apparently teleological development; this Darwin reduces to mere calculable chance, to the fact that in the average, the slight, accidental, directionless variations (today we must say mutations) among the thousands of millions of individuals who are born and die are retained and passed on to the progeny if and only if they are of some slight advantage to the individual in its struggle for existence, while they are eliminated if they are disadvantageous. Thus teleo-

[4] "The Statistical Law of Nature," *Nature* (London), CLIII (1944), 704.

logical lines of development arise through calculable chance.

The mechanical theory of heat similarly bases the laws of physics and chemistry on calculable chance. Most of these laws are far sharper and more exact than the organic-lines of development we have been discussing. But this again is no mystery. The greater the number of individual cases a statistic is based on, the clearer and the more reproducible its results will be. According to the mechanical theory of heat, almost every individual phenomenon we observe in nature is itself the result of the interplay of an enormous number of atoms and molecules and their collisions, etc. And the number of particular events that work together in the slightest phenomenon that we observe—that work together in accordance with pure calculable chance—is in general far higher than in the field of biology, running not into millions but into millions of billions of billions. This alone is the reason why, if we repeat the same observation under the same conditions, we again observe the same phenomenon, quantitatively unchanged. Today this is no longer a dubious hypothesis; we are dealing with facts that can be checked in all significant details, merely by setting up conditions in which the number of particular occurrences contributing to an observable phenomenon is not too enormous. The theory permits us to calculate in advance the exact degree of indeterminateness and irreproducibility in such a phenomenon, and this lack of precision finds exact quantitative confirmation in experiment.

Boltzmann's theory of natural law casts an interesting sidelight on the concept of time. I shall come back to this (see 6 below).

### 4

Let us now advance to the threshold of the twentieth century. It so happens that exactly in 1900 two completely new leitmotivs were sounded, which proved to be the two leading ideas of modern physics and biology respectively. In this year, Max Planck laid before the Prussian Academy his work on the theory of heat radiation, which subsequently led to the quantum theory. In the same year, the Mendelian laws of heredity were rediscovered and their far-reaching importance recognized, independently by Tschermak in Vienna, de Vries in Leyden, and Correns in Berlin. Soon thereafter, Mendel's ideas were extended in de Vries's theory of mutations. The history of the world-famous dissertation of the Augustinian abbot, which slumbered in the archives of the Scientific Society of Brünn from 1866 to 1900, is today generally known. An old friend of mine, a physicist, has given me a charming detail. Soon after the rediscovery, he took the volume in question from the library of his academy and found that the pages had not even been cut.

Now let us consider the reorientation in physics brought about by the work of Max Planck. This is one of the cases where, in pursuing the underlying idea, we shall do better not to follow the historical development exactly. Planck's discovery that energy was not transmitted between material systems in a steady, continuous stream, as had been believed, but apparently in definite amounts, or "quanta" —this discovery represented for the physicist an extraordinarily exciting and challenging paradox. Indeed, Planck himself was slow and reluctant to accept the revolutionary implications of his discovery, and kept searching for ways to avoid them. Yet this whole matter is so far removed from ordinary thinking that it is difficult to perceive its full profundity and import at first glance. But aside from the theory of radiation there is another approach to the new orientation in physics which brings it into a meaningful historical context that is hundreds, indeed thousands, of years old. This approach is the discovery made by Einstein some years later that energy and mass are merely different aspects of the same thing, that they are indeed identical.

Energy is a dynamic concept—at first sight a very abstract one—to which we are led when we submit to mathematical analysis the interplay of forces by which different parts of matter affect each other's movements, as, for example, the sun and the planets and moons. To the mathematical physicist energy is primarily nothing more

than an integration constant (a very important one, to be
sure) in the equations of mechanical motion. Later heat
was also found to be a 'form of energy', since in actual
physical motion the 'constant' of energy is usually not
constant but diminishes, while somewhere a certain quantity of heat is always produced. But according to the
mechanical theory of heat, of which I have already spoken,
heat is nothing more than the motion of the smallest particles of matter. The 'inconstancy of the constant' is only
apparent. A part of it slips into the hidden motion of the
smallest particles. Up to a certain degree, the process can
be reversed and the energy regained through certain con-
trivances such as heat-driven engines. Thus energy, though
in a strictly mathematical sense not identical with motion,
is, as a concept, equivalent to motion and to force gen-
erating motion.

Mass, on the other hand, is the essential characteristic
of matter. Newton, by a naïve tautology, still defined mass
as *quantitas materiae*. A better Latin word for it would be
*moles*. For what we think of first in connexion with mass
is the inertia with which a body resists being set in motion
by forces.

It was believed for a long time that to contrast energy
and mass, or in older terms force and matter, was very
fundamental. We remember Büchner's well-known work,
which to be sure belongs to a rather dubious philosophical
milieu. This belief did not always enjoy undivided support. At all times there have been some profound thinkers
who were disturbed by the duality of force and matter,
who sensed in the *vires* a mystery from which they tried to
free themselves. I believe that even Democritus, with his
theory of atoms, was obscurely aiming at the ideal of
deriving a purely geometrical view of the whole natural
process from the fixed size and shape of the atoms that
collide and deflect each other in virtue of their mutual
impenetrability. Certainly Descartes's views tended toward
geometrization, which, by the way, was the forerunner of
the modern theories of relativity. Perhaps I shall be able
to devote a few more words to it later on.

But now to Einstein's discovery; his famous equation

$$E = M$$

(energy equals mass) has put an end once and for all to the duality of force and matter. In view of what I have said before about energy and mass, it appears paradoxical in the highest degree to equate them. But today this is no longer an hypothesis, it is unhappily for the world an indubitable fact. For the enormous energy produced by the atom bomb results from a relatively slight diminution in the mass of the substances involved; i.e., the substances resulting from the alchemistic reaction weigh slightly less than the original substances. I say alchemistic, because a transformation of elements actually takes place, and this transformation is accompanied by a loss of mass. The lost mass ultimately reappears as heat and produces the inconceivably high temperature.

Thus the fact is clear, though in this simple form it is of course purely programmatic. We must delve into its meaning, which implies an immense programme. It will compel us to organize our view—our *theōría*—of nature in such a way as to obviate force as an explicit concept, retaining it merely as an auxiliary concept. Einstein in his *Meaning of Relativity* has already done this for the theory of gravitation; he has done it through geometrization, though in an entirely different way from what Democritus and Descartes may have conceived. But of this I hope I shall be able to say more later.

Now let us turn in another direction. After what has been said, it will not be hard for you to recognize the nature of Planck's famous quanta of energy. In view of Einstein's equation they turn out to be quanta of mass. The idea of the discontinuity of matter, the idea that it is not continuous but consists of discrete particles, has been familiar to us since Democritus. Since Democritus, the notion has never been entirely lost, although many thinkers were violently opposed to it up to the very end—that is, up to the time when incontrovertible experiments proved the soundness of the atomic theory.

Now we need simply transfer this discontinuity, this discreteness, from mass to energy: and there we have

Planck's quantum theory. Of course it is not as simple as all that. This view of the physical world remains a revolution, and we are in the midst of it. How shall we conceive as discrete and discontinuous all the phenomena that have hitherto been regarded as the steady effect of a force that imparts, let us say, a gradually increasing velocity to a particle of mass? How shall we do so without sacrificing the clear, simple ideas that were contained in the older conception and which were very well adapted to explaining a large complex of facts that had been confirmed by experiment?—These ideas we must preserve unharmed. This is possible only if, on the basis of Einstein's equation, we also inversely transfer certain conceptions and working methods from the older theory of force to what used to be known as matter. An understanding of wireless transmission, of light, even of the simplest electrical apparatus such as the dynamo, the electric motor, the transformer, requires indispensably the conception of forces and waves continuously traversing space. But since on the other hand we must now adhere to the conception of energy exchanged in quanta, we arrive at a twofold nature of phenomena, which at first seems somewhat uncomfortable. Regardless how we ultimately reconcile ourselves to this twofold nature, we shall not obtain a general picture unless we ascribe such a twofold nature to particles of mass properly speaking, i.e., to those quanta of energy which we have always known as discontinuous and only as discontinuous. We must associate waves with particles of mass. But here I must warn against a common misunderstanding. Neither our imagination nor our linguistic usage is adequate to the comprehension and expression of so novel an idea. The meaning here is not that the particles of matter generate forces or waves, nor that they are surrounded by waves, but that they themselves can be regarded as waves, that they *are* waves.

But let us turn from these difficulties which, despite great partial successes, have not yet been solved and upon which I have scarcely time to touch, and turn back to our leitmotiv, the discontinuity or discreteness which, two thousand years after it was discovered or at least surmised for 'matter', has been extended to force, so that in some way it will come to dominate our entire conception of nature.

Now what is so significant in this idea? Simply this, that discrete things can be counted; they can be counted with the help of the simplest, clearest mathematical equipment, of perhaps the one mathematical concept that is fully understood, the integer.[5] This allows us to hope for a real understanding, free from mystery, of many things that formerly we could only describe, or register as experienced. Boltzmann's theory of natural law, which I have characterized as one of the two great achievements of the nineteenth century, rests entirely on the method of counting discrete things, to wit, atoms, molecules, and their collisions. At first the method appeared rather accidental, a lucky chance. Cases were even found in which it was inapplicable, or applicable only with difficulty—with liquids, for example, because the molecules are so densely packed that it is impossible to speak of separate collisions, since every molecule is in constant interaction with dozens of neighbours. But the universality of discreteness, as now recognized, appears to show that the method of enumeration, the method of the integer, is really the royal road, the only road by which we may hope to achieve real insight.

5

This view is confirmed when we realize that a truly astonishing inner kinship exists between the idea just stated and the second great scientific field that was opened to us in the fruitful year 1900: that of modern genetics.

Here, too, continuity has been replaced by discontinuity. The attention of biologists has shifted from the small, almost imperceptible variations of the phenotype, conceived by Darwin, to the mutations of the genotype, also small but discrete and therefore enumerable; the former, though they appear in the individual, are not transmissible, only the latter represent an hereditary change (precisely this

---

[5] Leopold Kronecker: 'Integers were made by God, everything else is the work of man.'

consideration is expressed in the Greek technical terms). Thus the theory of mutations is an atomic theory of heredity. It is for the understanding of the origin of species what the quantum theory is for physcis: the transformation does not take place evenly but in little jumps. That is so; it is a simple fact, not an idea. This fact enables us to count and thus for the first time to introduce an exact quantitative, mathematical method—indeed, the most exact of all—into the field of biology, so incomparably more complex than that of physics. Physics and chemistry on the one hand and biology on the other now approach one another to a degree and in a way which could never have been foreseen. Just as the physicochemist begins to realize that his 'laws' are not really exact and inviolable, but follow merely from the law of averages; just as he is overcome by enthusiasm because he is enabled to corroborate his thesis and in cases where the numbers are not too large, really to observe the exceptions to his rigid 'laws': at this very moment the biologist, the geneticist, is no less overjoyed to find that exact laws do exist in his field—even though, he says almost apologetically, they are 'only' statistical laws, which become more and more exact as the number of subjects investigated increases.—Is there still any basic difference?—No.

I have explained elsewhere that this is no mere outward similarity between the sciences, no methodological analogy, but a direct, inner, essential connexion in so far as the mutations are real, though sometimes exceedingly complex quantum transitions. A detailed discussion of this would lead us too far. But I should like to add one observation which seems to me of interest, though it quite possibly represents nothing more than an analogy.

In physics today we see relatively clearly that our conception of the atomism of matter and energy is somewhat too naïve, although we do not yet know how to improve on it. The particles are not separate entities of ascertainable individuality. Somehow the concept of the field enters into the picture, connecting the particles, interchanging their rôles in a way that cannot be verified, and so on.

It is hard to express oneself clearly in the matter, because we do not yet understand it.

But it is highly interesting to note that recently a reaction has set in against the rigid atomism of heredity in the Mendel-Morgan theory. This reaction has given rise to the idea of 'positional effect', according to which the genes are not strictly localized parts of the chromosome, with individuals responsible for this or that trait or mutation; the mutations are brought about by complex structural characteristics in the chromosome as a whole.

I know too little about this to say any more. It is possible that the common trait in the two developments can be reduced to the general rule that in every great discovery one tends to overshoot the mark and that, as in artillery fire, the next step is a process of range finding.

6

The time is growing short and I must abandon the greater part of the programme we drew up at the start. Concerning the geometrization of force in the theories of relativity, I shall have some little to say a few days from now in Zurich.[6] The cosmic problem would in itself occupy at least a long lecture; concerning point 8, something is to be found in my little book *What Is Life?*:[7] much more than what I have written there I myself do not know.

And so I should like to ask your attention just a little while longer for a few sidelights that scientific thought has cast on the concept of time, because contemporary writers have seldom given this point (so important in the history of ideas) the attention it deserves.

The essential with regard to time is our knowledge of earlier and later. The seems to be a commonplace, almost a tautology. Therefore it will perhaps not be superfluous to point out the following: We are, it is true, accustomed

[6] Published in *Verhandlungen der Schweizer Naturforschenden Gesellschaft* (Zurich, 1946), 53–61.

[7] New York and Cambridge, 1944 (and the first essay in the present volume).

to conceive of the subjective passage of time in the individual as a complete, indubitable, and well-ordered chain of experiences. But sometimes when we attach real importance to a decision regarding earlier or later, we find out that we cannot arrive at it intuitively, but must resort to rational inferences.

When was I given this paperweight that lies on my table? I recollect. I remember a remark that my friend X made about it the first time he saw it. But X hasn't been to see me in my own house since I lived in Zurich. The answer is therefore: in Zurich, or even earlier.—Each one of us is familiar with hundreds of instances of this kind of reasoning. Not to mention dreams, which *subjectively* are equivalent to the waking state. Here the time sequence is often completely confused, we speak with people who have long been dead. We worry about their future, and so on.

The wide-spread belief that the earlier and later of any two events is absolute and indubitable is therefore based not on immediate, subjective evidence, but on physics and chronology: on good watches, on a calendar approved by the state, and on the traces of individual and common experience that each day and each hour leaves in tens of thousands of newspapers, court records, official records, diaries, dated personal letters, etc. Thence we come to look upon the earlier-later relationship as an objective reality, independent of any records or other traces and inherent in the events themselves. Perhaps no trace can be found, but still one may exist. In the place and time in which a given event occurs, certain traces, repercussions, effects, of some other event may already be present. And we feel certain that if this possibility exists, the opposite possibility is excluded. According to this rational criterion we then call the 'other event' the earlier.

Here we see that the concept of time is closely bound up with the causal connexion of the world: the earlier event can affect the later event, not the other way round. When the special theory of relativity limited the sphere of causality very considerably by revealing that no physical cause could spread more rapidly than with the speed of light, our old, naïve concept of time had to be considerably revised. Consider two events, 'simultaneous' in the naïve sense, taking place at A and B. A certain time must elapse before an effect from A can reach B.[8] Conversely, the event at B would have had to take place at an equal interval earlier, in order for an effect from B to have reached A. This double time interval at B embraces all the conceivable events at B which from the standpoint of the causal connexion are neither earlier nor later than the event at A. But it further develops that the 'simultaneous' event at B has no prerogative, no better right to be considered simultaneous with the event at A, than any other event occurring at B during the double time interval.

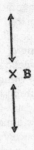

For places on the earth, this time interval is never greater than the fraction of a second. For cosmic distances the interval of sumultaneity can amount to many years or even millennia.

From this conception, which is today uncontested, no very clear philosophical inference can be drawn. On the contrary, its significance lies perhaps in that it has blurred for the first time the supposed clarity of the space-time pattern by which man had always contemplated the universe, and shaken our faith in the monopoly of this pattern.

Suppose a friend of mine should board a space ship travelling at half the speed of light and reach the nearest fixed star in eight or ten years. Suppose he settled down

[8] The double-pointed arrows in the figure symbolize the two intervals of uncertainty.

there. At a certain moment I might wonder whether he were still alive, and I should have to realize that perhaps there is no objective answer to such a question. If he 'has died', but only recently, so that a radio message carrying the news cannot yet have reached me, or if he is only 'seriously ill' and 'going to die' before my next radiogram can reach him—in both cases, it is, from the standpoint of a physicist, a question of interpretation whether my friend is alive or not.

However, a far more incisive critique of the traditional concept of time comes to us from an entirely different source. But for a few exceptions, which really are exceptions, all events in nature are irreversible. A sequence of phenomena exactly opposite to that of real observation— as in a film run backwards—would almost always present a crass contradiction to natural laws. The most admired achievement of the mechanical theory was to make this specific direction of the world process really intelligible, intelligible without any *ad hoc* hypotheses embodied in the basic premises. According to Boltzmann, this direction is explained by the trivial circumstance that order 'tends' to be transformed into disorder, but not the other way around. Conceive of a deck of cards in perfect order, 7, 8, 9, 10, jack, queen, king, ace, in all four suits. A violent shuffling motion would (probably) transform it from this condition into one of complete disorder. Now, mechanically speaking, the exact same motion might change it back again from disorder to order. But everyone would expect the former transformation and no one will expect the latter—for which one would wait in vain.

I must beg your pardon for the sketchy character of this explanation. In any event, the spontaneous transition from order to disorder is the quintessence of Boltzmann's theory of natural law and the temporal direction inherent in any natural law. This theory really grants an understanding and does not beg the question. For any attempt to reason away the observed dissymmetry of things by means of an a priori sense of direction or a line of direction of the time variables must be regarded as a begging of the question. No one who has once understood Boltzmann's theory will ever again have recourse to such expedients. It would be a scientific regression beside which a repudiation of Copernicus in favor of Ptolemy would seem trifling.

At first we may find it astonishing that nevertheless objections to the theory have been raised again and again in the course of the past decades, and not by fools but by fine thinkers. If we carefully consider these objections and eliminate the subtle misunderstandings and false inferences, we actually find remaining a small but exceedingly significant residue which we might express as follows:

First, my good friend, you state that the two directions of your time variables, from $-t$ to $+t$ and from $+t$ to $-t$, are a priori equivalent. Then by fine arguments appealing to common sense you show that disorder (or 'entropy') must with overwhelming probability increase with time. Now, if you please, what do you mean by 'with time'? Do you mean in the direction $-t$ to $+t$? But if your inferences are sound, they are equally valid for the direction $+t$ to $-t$. If these two directions are equivalent a priori, then they remain so a posteriori. The conclusions can never invalidate the premise. Then your inference is valid for both directions of time, and that is a contradiction.

Now it is not as bad as all that. But there is only one way out. It is not true that the inference must be valid for both directions of time, it must only be valid for either one of the two. For which one is irrelevant. It is irrelevant whether we begin with the plus or the minus sign. That it is the direction from past to future we must state by definition.

In a word, we must decide once and for all to determine the direction of time by means of Boltzmann's theory itself. The increasing disorder is itself the adequate measure of advancing time. Only as long as the statistical theory of heat itself is allowed to determine where the past lies and where the future, can it be maintained. It collapses as soon as there is any other independent criterion for the direction of time.

If we pursue these considerations, as Boltzmann himself

did in full awareness of their implications, we may well be overcome by a slight dizziness—a dizziness in time, one might say. Boltzmann speaks seriously of the possibility that elsewhere in the universe time might run in the opposite direction, if the universe extended far enough in space and time.

This presumably it does not. It is not certain but fairly probable that straight lines run back into themselves after a distance of $10^{27}$ or at most $10^{30}$ centimeters and that the universe has not existed for more than $10^9$ or $10^{10}$ years in a state bearing any resemblance to its present state. These dimensions are far too small to leave room for the extravagance of an occasional reversal of time.

Yet the fact remains that time no longer appears to us as a gigantic, world-dominating *chrónos,* nor as a primitive entity, but as something derived from phenomena themselves. It is a figment of my thinking. That as such it might some day put an end to my thinking, as some believe, is beyond my comprehension. Even the old myth makes Kronos devour only his own children, not his begetter.

# INDEX

# ANCHOR BOOKS